Optimum Sustainable Yield
as a Concept in
Fisheries Management

The Symposium on Optimum Sustainable Yield was sponsored by the American Fisheries Society, the National Oceanic and Atmospheric Administration of the United States Department of Commerce, and the Sport Fishing Institute.

Financial support for the symposium and for this publication was provided by NOAA Office of Sea Grant, Department of Commerce, under Grant No. 04-5-158-31. The U.S. Government is authorized to produce and distribute reprints for governmental purposes notwithstanding any copyright notation that may appear herein.

Optimum Sustainable Yield as a Concept in Fisheries Management

Philip M. Roedel

Editor

Proceedings of a Symposium
Held During the 104th Annual Meeting
of the American Fisheries Society
Honolulu, Hawaii, September 9, 1974

Special Publication No. 9
American Fisheries Society
Washington, D. C.
1975

Library of Congress Catalog Card Number: 75-10992

All orders should be addressed to

American Fisheries Society

1319 18th Street, N. W.

Washington, D. C. 20036

Printed in the United States of America

by Allen Press, Inc., Lawrence, Kansas

Contents

Preface

The traditional view of maximum sustainable yield as the philosophic base for fisheries management programs has come under increasing attack over the last decade or so. Economists were first to take issue with the concept, arguing in favor of a formula designed to give the greatest economic return rather than the greatest amount of protein.

Over a period of time, a variety of people joined the economists for a variety of reasons not necessarily associated with economics. Sportsmen leaders were early and prominent figures, but there were also adherents from commercial fisheries and a growing number of fisheries biologists and administrators. Many of these people suggested optimum sustainable yield, or simply optimum yield, as a still better guiding precept. This was particularly true of those who were interested in social as well as biological and economic values. The propounders, however, pretty much failed to define what they meant by optimum.

The opportunity arose to debate the issues at the 104th Annual Meeting of the American Fisheries Society under the joint sponsorship of the American Fisheries Society, the National Oceanic and Atmospheric Administration, and the Sport Fishing Institute. Richard H. Stroud, Executive Vice-President of the Sport Fishing Institute, agreed to organize and chair the session, which quickly developed into a major symposium concerned with yield concepts.

The notice was short, but it proved possible to convene a multidisciplinary group of distinguished experts representing the academic community, sport and commercial fishing interests, and state and federal governmental agencies.

The symposium's agenda provided for presentation of a series of invited formal contributions, a period during which questions and comments were entertained from the floor, a panel discussion, and a closing summary critique. The papers in this volume include those prepared in advance by the principal speakers, those submitted for publication by the panelists based on their more unstructured remarks, and the summary critique.

All the participants acted in their capacities as independent experts, and their comments may or may not represent the views of their parent organizations. None of the papers have been edited or refereed on matters of substance.

Neither the symposium itself nor this publication would have been possible without the support of the sponsors, each of which filled a role critical to success. AFS provided the appropriate public forum and the vehicle for publication, NOAA underwrote travel and publication costs, while SFI gave staff support before and after the meeting and, most importantly, provided the symposium with its organizer and chairman.

The fisheries community is indebted to these organizations.

Philip M. Roedel, *Editor*
Washington, D.C.
December, 1974

Introductory Remarks

Richard H. Stroud

It has become increasingly evident since mid-century, following the close of World War II, that the earlier *laissez-faire* approach to marine fisheries development is inadequate to serve the needs of both the commercial fishing industry and the general public. This changing attitude in marine fisheries affairs was reflected in the 1958 Oceans Convention, formulated under United Nations auspices at Geneva, where the term "Optimum Sustainable Yield" (OSY) was formally invoked as the basic concept of marine fisheries management. At that time, the context of deliberations involved chiefly the narrow goal of securing "a maximum supply of food" from the renewable ocean resources.

In most fresh waters of the United States, except the Great Lakes, the situation has long been largely reversed—indeed, since colonial times—with the goal of aquatic production being primarily to serve recreational fisheries needs. At the same time, there has been more or less universal accommodation of commercial fishing enterprise so long as it did not interfere or conflict seriously with the recreational fisheries. Where such conflicts have developed to an intolerable level, state or federal legislation has been enacted to solve the problem. The most far-reaching example of the latter was the enactment, in 1926, of the famous federal Black Bass Act that effectively ended commercial exploitation of one of America's leading families of game fishes.

At Auburn University in the early 1940's, the late Homer Swingle and his associates commenced a farm pond fisheries research program that soon threw much light on the dynamics of simple and complex fish populations, produced over relatively short periods of time, in small artificially-controlled bodies of water. Among other provocative findings, Swingle (1950) propounded a series of ratios among various components of his experimental fish populations by which fish managers might judge pond "balance" (or imbalance). Pond "balance" was defined in terms of various criteria contributing to a state of satisfactory fishing. The latter, in turn, was a function of several factors, including (1) minimum sizes of various species of fish that would be voluntarily retained by anglers as acceptable sizes, and (2) the frequency of catching those acceptably sized fish.

Here, then, was one of the earlier organized attempts by fisheries researchers in the United States to measure and quantify some biological and economic factors in terms of specific fish management objectives that included elements other than mere protein production alone. Swingle's bold initiatives generated controversy that shook, to its very foundations, the inland branch of the fish management profession. Significantly, those novel approaches stimulated many other workers in later years to think outside traditional lines. It was from precisely mid-century, therefore, that inland fisheries workers have undertaken increasingly to broaden their fisheries management practices to accommodate economic and social objectives as well as strictly biological goals. This favorable development is reflected in the widespread elimination of closed seasons on most warmwater species in most situations; the setting of catch-and-release regulations for various species, especially trout, to promote "trophy" fishing in selected situations; the introduction of predatory species to convert abundant non-game species into economically-valuable sport species; et cetera.

Suffice it to say that inland fisheries managers, primarily concerned with meeting the needs of the recreational fisheries, have tended since about 1950 to apply the concept of optimum sustainable yield to their efforts, by adding social and economic factors to traditional biological considerations. According to

Webster's New International Dictionary, (Unabridged, Second Edition, 1960), "optimum" means the "best; most favorable or most conducive to a given end, especially, under fixed conditions." Thus we approach a subject, today, that must be regarded as imprecise because it is judgmental in nature. Our problem would seem, in part, to require a definition of the particular "fixed conditions" that may be applicable. One of the overriding "fixed conditions" with respect to the recreational fisheries, of course, is that the fishing is done by single hook and line. It is not done by means of the many times more efficient longlines and nets that are customarily employed in commercial fishing.

The concept of optimum sustainable yield best accommodates the elusive but highly important element of "quality" in recreational fishing. Though not universally defined or quantified, the concept of "quality" obviously includes considerations of variety in angling experiences. The species caught, the sizes of the fish involved, the situations in which they are found, and the method by which they are sought or harvested are some such considerations. It seems evident that a conservation concept that seeks merely to produce a maximum yield of protein, for direct or indirect nourishment of the physical human body, will not adequately accommodate either the purposes of the recreational fisheries or the needs of the troubled commercial fisheries.

Some recent broadening of heretofore rigid federal government adherence to the narrow concept of maximum sustainable yield (MSY) seems to be reflected in the revision of the United States fisheries position that was announced at the recent Law of the Sea Conference. The new position was reflected in new Draft Articles on the Economic Zone and Continental Shelf, tabled by the U. S. August 8, 1974. Article 12, on Conservation proposes, establishes allowable catches to maintain or restore populations of harvested species "at levels which can produce the maximum sustainable yield, taking into account relevant environmental and economic factors ..." That article states further, that ". . . such measures shall take into account effects of species associated with or dependent upon harvested

species . . ." This would appear to come out, on balance, as one possible definition of "optimum sustainable yield."

A recent deliberate attempt at such a definition is contained in the Senate Commerce Committee Report (No. 93-1079; August 8, 1974; page 22) on S. 1988, the Magnuson bill to establish an interim 200-mile marine fisheries jurisdictional zone. It defines OSY as ". . . the largest net economic return consistent with the biological capabilities of the stock, as determined on the basis of all relevant economic, biological, and environmental factors."

It is with these and other considerations in mind that the American Fisheries Society, The National Oceanic and Atmospheric Administration (NOAA), and the Sport Fishing Institute have joined together in presenting this Symposium. NOAA is underwriting the cost of the Symposium with the help of its Sea Grant Program. We are especially indebted to the distinguished Principal Speakers who, at considerable personal sacrifice with respect to the added burden of restricted time for preparation, have consented to present papers addressing various aspects of this important subject. We appreciate equally the willingness of the well-qualified Special Panelists, who have agreed to respond briefly to the presentations by the Principal Speakers.

The Principal Speakers, in their order of appearance on the Program, are as follows:

Mr. David H. Wallace, Associate Administrator for Marine Resources, National Oceanic and Atmospheric Administration, U. S. Department of Commerce, Rockville, Maryland;

Dr. William F. Royce, Associate Director for Resource Research, National Marine Fisheries Service, National Oceanic and Atmospheric Administration, U. S. Department of Commerce, Washington, D. C.;

Dr. James A. Crutchfield, Professor, Department of Economics, University of Washington, Seattle, Washington;

Mr. John Radovich, Chief, Operations Research Branch, California Department of Fish and Game, The Resources Agency, Sacramento, California;

Dr. Richard O. Anderson, Leader, Cooperative Fishery Research Unit, the U. S. Fish and

Wildlife Service and the University of Missouri, Columbia, Missouri;

Mr. Robert G. Mauermann, Executive Director, Texas Shrimp Association and Shrimp Association of the Americas, Brownsville, Texas;

Dr. Frank Carlton, President, National Coalition for Marine Conservation, Savannah, Georgia; and

Dr. John P. Harville, Executive Director, Pacific Marine Fisheries Commission, Portland, Oregon.

The Special Panelists who will respond to the formal presentations by the Principal Speakers, in order of their commentary, are:

Dr. Thomas L. Linton, Director, Office of Marine Affairs, North Carolina Department of Administration, Raleigh, North Carolina;

Dr. Salvatore Comitini, Associate Professor, Department of Economics, University of Hawaii at Manoa, Honolulu, Hawaii;

Mr. Frank K. Goto, General Manager, United Fishing Agency, Ltd., Honolulu, Hawaii;

Mr. Frank L. Cassidy, Vice President of Son Sales, Ltd., Portland, Oregon, a building materials distributor; residing in Vancouver, Washington, he is a national vice president of Trout Unlimited and the Northwest Steelheaders Association, and a current member of the Washington State Game Commission; and

Mr. Richard S. Croker, Retired fisheries administrator, Laguna Niguel, California.

The distinguished Summarizer for the Symposium is *Mr. Philip Roedel*, Coordinator, Marine Recreation Programs, National Oceanic and Atmospheric Administration, U. S. Department of Commerce, Rockville, Maryland.

Literature Cited

SWINGLE, H. S. 1950. Relationships and dynamics of balanced and unbalanced fish populations. Ala. Agr. Exp. Sta. Bull. 274. 73pp.

Sport Fishing Institute, 608 13th Street, N.W., (Suite 801) Washington, D.C. 20005

Keynote Address

David H. Wallace

I am delighted to have the opportunity to address this symposium, for the subject we are discussing here today will have a substantial impact on future policy considerations in fisheries management—especially marine fisheries management. I am looking forward to hearing what our expert panelists have to say, but also we all will be listening carefully to comments you in the audience will be making during the discussions.

We live in a world of rapid change. We no longer can continue to do things the same old way as we have done in the past. When commercial fishermen throughout the world were taking 25,000,000 tons of fish from all oceans, and obviously not utilizing all of the species available, the needs for comprehensive management were minimal. Few management requirements were imposed except for a very limited number of species, since most stocks were underutilized and fishing could be increased without much cause for concern.

In the past decade or two, the world fishing situation has changed dramatically. Massive development of distant-water fleets has resulted in the capability of such fleets to operate anywhere in the world, supplying their own logistic support. The ocean catch has risen quickly to 70,000,000 tons. World fisheries are fast approaching the point where all the well-defined stocks of fish will be fully utilized. In the course of doing this, some important fish stocks are being depleted in the absence of adequate management measures. Policy decisions must be made and effective management regimes established if we are to maintain ocean fish stocks at a high level of abundance, so that they can be utilized, over time, to the best advantage. This best advantage will be viewed very differently, on the one hand by an underdeveloped country desperately in need of protein, and on the other hand by a country, such as the United States, where protein is not as pressing a problem now and where opportunities for recreation must be provided. It is in this context that I wish to approach this entire matter of discussing a basis for management.

My interest and involvement in fisheries management techniques extend over many years, back to the early 1940's. At that time, Bob Nesbit, of the old United States Bureau of Commercial Fisheries, was advocating the concept of controlling the number of fishermen, but then allowing each fisherman to operate efficiently in terms of effort. This concept was developed in the absence of a clearly defined technique to determine the safe level of the catch. But this was such a revolutionary concept that few took it seriously. Most fisheries managers were trained as biologists, lawyers, or, often, in politics—but most certainly not in economics. Recognizing that fishery resources were renewable, but not inexhaustible, biologists investigated the characteristics of fish populations to determine whether or not it would be possible to find a rate of exploitation that would maintain a given resource at a high level of production. The central concern, as biologist-managers, was to prevent the overexploitation of fisheries resources and to preserve the productivity of the resources for the future. Biologists tended to regard any unused surplus as waste. Thus, the concept of MSY (maximum sustainable yield) evolved, representing a sort of average of the highest potential surplus that is likely to be produced by a given fishery stock. This approach seemed to work fairly well, particularly in our inshore fisheries. MSY came to be considered a relevant and non-controversial objective of conservation—just about the final word in terms of management.

In the United States, as demands for fisheries resources increased, user and allocation conflicts developed. Gear conflicts arose between commercial fishermen; regional and state conflicts occurred; and, of course, conflicts between sport and commercial fishermen increased. When distant-water fleets appeared, immediate conflicts developed between those foreign fishermen off our shores and the domestic local fishermen who had come to look upon these coastal stocks as belonging to them exclusively. To compound the problem, the fishermen's profit diminished and sportsmen, in many cases, had little success. These adverse events attracted the attention of the economists. They began to talk and write about the need to consider various economic factors in fisheries management. Some even suggested that the management of fisheries should be undertaken for the benefit of man—not fish. These concepts tended to disturb fisheries biologists, especially when economists began to talk in terms of maximum economic efficiency at a level of harvest generally conceded to be below MSY. Nevertheless, the concept brought a whole new dimension to the discussion of fisheries management and, in my opinion is now generally accepted in the United States as part of the fisheries management requirements. But even this development did not fully satisfy management needs.

The need to consider social implications became apparent as we began to become more aware of general public desires and especially the impact of marine sport fishing. Consideration of sport fishing requirements brought into focus still another factor in fisheries management philosophy—the elusive but important element of "quality" in sport fishing. This concept began to be expressed rather vaguely in terms of optimum sustainable yield or optimum yield. The term "optimum sustainable yield" gained acceptance during the 1958 International Convention on Law of the Sea in Geneva, Switzerland, where conservation was defined as ". . . the aggregate of the measures rendering possible the optimum sustainable yield from those resources so as to secure a maximum supply of food and other marine products . . .".

At the 1974 International Convention on Law of the Sea in Caracas, Venezuela, from which I have recently returned, the strong position on the part of most countries, and particularly the developing ones, was expressed as a move toward complete control of the fisheries resources along their coasts.

The United States, in its new articles on fisheries[1] in support of the 200-mile economic zone, made a requirement that the coastal state shall ensure the conservation of renewable resources within the economic zone. To attain this goal, the following principles shall be applied:

(1) to maintain or restore populations of harvested species at levels which can produce the maximum sustainable yield, taking into account relevant environmental and economic factors, and any generally agreed global and regional minimum standards;

(2) such measures shall take into account effects on species associated with or dependent upon harvested species and at a minimum, shall be designed to maintain or restore populations of such associated or dependent species above levels at which they may become threatened with extinction; . . .

Other articles cover special arrangements for management of anadromous and high seas migratory species.

It is appropriate, I feel, to explore the whole question of optimum yield and what it can mean in terms of United States fishery management policies in the immediate future. The Board of Directors of the Sport Fishing Institute, at their annual meeting this year, passed a resolution urging the substitution of the optimum yield concept in fishery management for the ". . . outmoded MSY concept . . .". Many fishery scientists do not consider the concept of MSY "outmoded" and were incensed at this attack. This strong feeling, in part, was reflected in the spirited exchange of letters last year in the "Items for Fishery Scientists" distributed by the Sport Fishing Institute.

In view of the controversial nature of this issue it seems essential to attempt to define and understand what exactly is meant by such terms as MSY, maximum economic efficiency (MEE), and optimum yield. Only then can the widely diversified views begin to be focused on a solution to the management decisions fac-

---

[1] United Nations, 3rd Conf. Law of the Sea. 1974. United States of America: draft articles for a chapter on the economic zone and the continental shelf. A/Conf.62/C.2/L.47. 11 p.

ing us. I should like to make a few observations on some of these points.

First, as a person originally trained in marine biology, I readily concede that important domestic fisheries have been severely depleted under fisheries management regimes based on MSY, but these failures must be put in their proper perspective. The concept of MSY cannot be blamed for the depletion of all the important stocks of fish. MSY is a tool by which the level of harvest can be determined. Whether or not this level is accepted and adhered to depends on the management regime. MSY is not the management regime; and in the past we have confused the difference between the tool for management and the actual management of the resource itself! For example, in the International Commission for the Northwest Atlantic Fisheries (ICNAF), where I am the United States Government commissioner and where I have been involved in some very diverse problems, the fisheries management concept has been modified to give additional consideration to optimum utilization of total biomass based on economic and technical factors and scientific investigations. Yet, many stocks in the Northwest Atlantic are in trouble because there has been "too little action too late."

Scientists warned for years that the MSY for these stocks was being exceeded. The problem is that, in this and almost all other international fishery agreements, we have lacked adequate institutional mechanisms to act forcefully on the information available. Frankly, without such a strong management regime, including a sound scientific and statistical information base, full authority to effect appropriate regulations and the mechanism and capability for equitable rigid enforcement on all participants in the fishery, any concept of fisheries management: MSY, MEE, or optimum yield, is destined to fail in the conservation of international fisheries resources. Many domestic fisheries management operations can be criticized for the same reason. I have avoided mentioning allocation of the resource here even though this process becomes an integral part of any management scheme. MSY, MEE, and optimum yield obviously do not address this matter.

Secondly, while I recognize that MSY by itself is not an acceptable management concept in the United States, it must still be recognized and accepted as an important tool of fishery scientists and managers. We need to know the MSY of any given stock before we can handle allocation and optimization. Further, as we become more sophisticated in our management, we must know the biomass and calculate the MSY for it. In the ICNAF area, as I have already indicated, our scientists are working toward this total biomass concept as a basis for management of the combined fish stocks.

Since I am unwilling to relegate MSY to the trash heap, I must add MEE to this list of things to be saved. Economists need this as a tool in certain special types of economic analyses and it will be helpful in supplying the managers of the future with input to decision making.

Now I would like to address briefly the term optimum yield. This is a vague term sometimes associated with economic factors, sometimes with both economic and biological. Nevertheless, as a modern approach to fisheries management to provide maximum public benefits to sport and commercial fishermen, it seems logical to manage on the basis of "optimum yield." Such a concept requires taking into account all the factors mentioned—economic, sociological, and biological—in determining the optimum level of harvest. It provides the flexibility essential to meet the diverse needs of the resource and the citizens who are to enjoy the benefits. I suspect that, in general, the results will be a level of fishing that would normally be below MSY but would provide for the special needs of special groups and the specific requirements for conservation of the target species.

It seems to me that the time has come to make some firm decisions on fisheries management. Are we going to face the issues mentioned heretofore?

Optimum yields cannot be the same for any given stock of fish, for every region of our coasts, or, indeed, for every season of the year. Certainly, it cannot be defined specifically for all groups of fishermen or even for an individual fisherman at all times. For example,

Joe Fisherman, a saltwater angler, usually takes his son fishing on a party boat for mackerel or porgies, or whatever happens to be biting that day. For that man and boy, the optimum yield is lots of action—their primary interest is not a trophy fish. Indeed, surveys have shown that this type of fishing is overwhelmingly indulged in by most sport fishermen. We must have a concept that insures this large group of citizens a fair share in the allocation. Finally, after careful saving, the same Joe Fisherman and his son may have the opportunity to go after marlin, or maybe chinook salmon. You can be sure, at that time the concept of the optimum yield for Joe will be a trophy fish that he can bring home to show all his friends.

Obviously, optimum yield has many complex components. Yet the quantification of such components should not be beyond the capability of economists and statisticians for they are already being forced to do these kinds of analyses in the evaluation of proposed environmental alterations, in calculating cost-benefit ratios for reservoirs, in coastal zone management programs, et cetera.

Let me point out that the optimum yield concept is of equal importance to the management of commercial fish stocks. A few examples will suffice. As many of you know, the haddock has been so badly depleted off New England that, in the interest of conservation, it has been necessary to impose a zero quota on the directed fishery for this species. This depletion has taken place even though ICNAF existed and was believed to have the power to control fishing. This reduction was brought about primarily by foreign fishing, but the adverse impact has affected our commercial fishermen far more than the foreigners who have the logistic capability to move elsewhere and fish on other stocks. Under a workable concept of optimum yield—and by "workable" I mean the institutional capability to implement and enforce—we would be able to optimize the haddock fishery, so that it could be rehabilitated rapidly, by reducing the harvest

of hake, cod, and other such species because such directed fisheries take great quantities of haddock as incidental catch. Thus, to optimize haddock fisheries in the interest of our haddock fishermen, the harvest of other species by other fishermen would be kept substantially below MSY. But the optimum yield for a haddock fisherman certainly will not be the optimum yield for a hake fisherman. Further, a decision to optimize haddok catches may not set well with hake fishermen, but administrators frequently must make unpopular decisions.

I wish to emphasize that any policy designed for the management of fisheries must be a deliberate and calculated course of action. Whether or not a particular policy leads to an increase in the total satisfaction of the members of society depends on the nature of the objective that is being sought and the constraints in the economic and social systems. In other words, the nature of the objective depends on the value judgments of the persons stipulating it. Since the objectives of fisheries management may differ among interests groups, the meaning of the optimal yield will also vary. But all must understand what the intent is—although some may not concur in the end product.

Quite clearly: economic, social, and biological values will serve as a basis for the statement of the objective. The optimal yield allows for these inputs, rather than being limited to maximizing net profits or maximizing sustainable yield.

It is essential that economists and other social scientists work with fisheries scientists to develop commonly accepted procedures for evaluating these kinds of subjective factors for both sport and commercial operations. I would hope that the panelists today, as well as those of you in the audience, can help us make important strides in this direction.

National Oceanic and Atmospheric Administration, United States Department of Commerce, Rockville, Maryland 20852

Use of Yield Models in Fishery Management[1]

William F. Royce

The purpose of this symposium is to discuss what people want as benefits from our living aquatic resources and how we should describe the goal of achieving them. We refer to that goal as the optimum sustainable yield; and I suggest that optimum means, in this case, the consensus of the people concerned with respect to what they want from a specific resource at a specific time. It is clear that the goal needs to be described in ways that make it attainable. It must be one that can be agreed upon by reasonable people, and it must be possible to attain it with the methods or instruments available.

I intend to direct my comments at the instruments available and especially at how the instruments should be used. They seem to have been dulled by misuse at times, and then, out of neglect, we have failed to use them when they would have served us well.

With few exceptions, the approach to fishery management, up to about the middle of this century, was based on the simple farm concept of protecting the broodstock and the young. When there was a shortage of fish, we reared fish artificially and stocked them. We established minimum size limits and prevented fishing during the spawning season or in spawning places. When the shortage persisted because too many people wanted to fish, we handicapped them with additional restraints on kind and amount of gear, the way in which it could be used, or the time and place in which it could be used.

With the development of ecological understanding, we began to develop the concept of ecological units or stocks from which we could take a sustainable yield. This concept, which is the focus of attention here, emerged as a useful instrument during the 1920's, '30's, and '40's. Baranof developed a yield-per-recruit model in 1918, but his work received little attention in fisheries until it was elaborated during the 1930's by Michael Graham, W. F. Thompson, J. Hjort, and later in the 1950's by W. E. Ricker, M. B. Schaefer, and the team of Beverton and Holt, to name only the leaders (Schaefer 1972). Since 1960 these pioneers have been followed by many others who have further developed the theory.

The application of the theories to management of the fisheries began primarily in the international fishery commissions where they have evolved as basic instruments in the annual cycle of negotiations.

The Models

The first model (Figure 1) that we should examine is simply the expected progress of the yield through time from the start of a fishery on a stock[2] of a food or recreational species. This has not been carefully averaged, but in the catch from many stocks we can identify first an exponential increase as fishermen learn to catch and market their product. Then comes a decline in the rate of increase as fishermen discover the full range of the stock and as accumulated stock is reduced. When the accumulated stock is gone and the fishery must depend solely on recruitment, the total yield frequently declines to a level of ⅓ to ½ the maximum if indeed a stable yield level is attained. It appears desirable from the standpoint of the resources as well as the users to gain control during the period of exponential increase in order to slow that increase and avoid the excess fishing effort that damages the stocks and bankrupts the fishermen.

Model number 2, and the first mathematical model (Figure 2), is the nearly parabolic ef-

---

[1] MARMAP Contribution No. 31.

[2] Stock is defined as a resource management unit. It is ideally an interbreeding group.

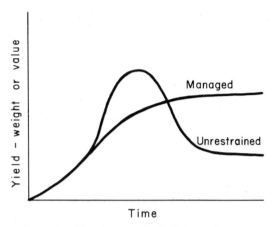

FIGURE 1. The time trends in fish catches.

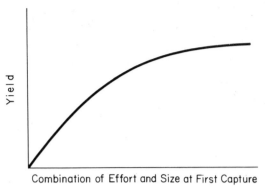

FIGURE 3. The yield per recruit.

fort-yield curve or general production model. It is the most general model because it is essentially a pragmatic description of the outcome of all of the interrelationships of recruitment, growth, and mortality.

Model number 3 is the yield per recruit curve of Beverton and Holt (Figure 3). I have simplified this to show on the abscissa merely the optimal combinations of fishing effort and size and at first capture. The curve tends to an asymptote rather than a maximum.

The relationship between stock size and recruitment (Figure 4) has proven to be the most troublesome to determine. It is subject to great variability, especially among the highly fecund species spawning in the open sea, and for the stocks of many such species the stock size has never been reduced enough to measure a reduced recruitment. Unfortunately, for a few stocks, such as cod, plaice, and herring, it has been possible to fill in the

lower end of the curve as recent data include stock sizes so low that recruitment is reduced (Cushing 1974).

What seems to be emerging is a family of curves in which recruitment is related to fecundity, to the size of parent stock, to density of eggs and larvae, and to density of predators. The highly fecund species such as cod or flounders that spawn in the very large area of the open sea have high average recruitment at very small stock sizes and a less abrupt decline at larger stock levels due to density. A moderately fecund species, such as a salmon spawning in a limited environment, shows a slower buildup of recruitment with increasing stock size and a more rapid decline due to density effects. The very low fecundity animals, such as elasmobranchs (Holden 1974) and mammals, show slow increase in recruitment directly related to population sizes as large as they have been studied, unless the breeding area is small. Density effects have been observed for mammals with small nurs-

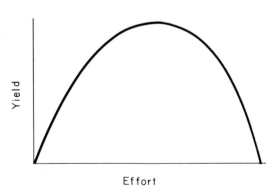

FIGURE 2. The effort-yield relationship.

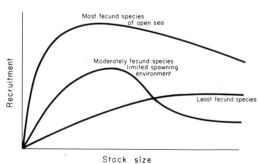

FIGURE 4. Some stock-recruitment relationships.

ery areas, but have not been recorded for elasmobranchs although they must occur at some population size. It is important to note that high fecundity apparently provides for greater resiliency against the effects of fishing.

The interpretation of the effort-yield models must always include consideration of the assumptions. The primary assumption is that the stock is a single interbreeding unit subject to ecological limitations on its maximum size and distribution which means that its size depends on its density. Almost equally important is the assumption of a steady state, free of environmental change or lag effects due to change in fishing effort.

These assumptions are rarely satisfied completely. Species commonly occur as clines over distances such that widely separated groups rarely interbreed, yet adjacent groups regularly interbreed but still retain some individual characteristics. Further, different species with similar habits may be so mixed in the fishery that they cannot be regulated separately, yet they never interbreed. Lastly, the steady state assumption is never satisfied completely. In some new fisheries it is never even approached as fishing proceeds rapidly enough to decimate the population in a few years.

The accuracy of our measures of population size and composition is frequently subject to challenge because of inadequate sampling. In order to compensate for the shortcomings of the mathematical models and to estimate long term effects, many modifications, frequently involving computer simulations, have been developed. These greatly increase the accuracy and kind of output from the models. They are too numerous and complicated to discuss here.

The Outputs from Yield Models

There has been so much attention given to the maximum sustainable average yield (MSAY) that it seems important to me to emphasize that such a figure is merely one of many items that can be obtained from the yield models or from the same data base that produces the yield models. In fact, in recent international negotiations, the MSAY is rarely a primary objective in the annual decisions. More important is an array of outputs to guide

the decisions. All of these outputs must be regarded as helping to forecast what to expect as to the yield from and condition of the resource with a given amount of fishing. These outputs include:

1. The identity of the stock: its composition, location, environmental requirements, and migrations. The definition of a stock requires a compromise between the ideal of a single interbreeding unit and the catch of a fishery that can be independently controlled. If the fishery is just starting, this information can help to speed development.

2. Sustainable average yield for a given level of effort. This includes a maximum as one of many points.

3. Marginal yield-per-unit change in effort. This is information that can readily be combined with economic or social data to estimate cost-benefit ratios.

4. Availability of the stock in different places and to different gear. This is important for allocating the catches among fishermen; e.g., recreational and commercial.

5. Expected by-catches. Because most gear catches more than a single species, the expected quantity of by-catch taken during the fishery for a given stock is needed, as well as the quantity of the given stock taken as a by-catch in other fisheries.

6. Effects of seasonal, sex, or size restraints. Such restraints can frequently augment the catch or effort limits to sustain the stocks or prevent waste.

7. Effects of environmental changes. Usually the fishing has a major effect on the stock—but not always—and sometimes the combined stress of heavy fishing and adverse environment may be especially harmful.

8. Unusual recruitment. All species have variable recruitment, but the highly fecund species spawning in the open sea may vary a hundredfold. It can be especially useful for the manager to plan optimum use of extra large and extra small year classes having in mind the needs of the resource as well as the users.

Management Decisions

The above are the instruments that fishery scientists can provide to the managers. These forecasts can be considered along with inputs from economic and social sciences to achieve an optimum sustainable average yield—if that can be defined objectively.

However, it may not be too important to define it precisely. The optimum will vary with time according to people's desires and a system of annual management decisions provides a recurring opportunity to consider all inputs. We should expect to improve the expected benefits in each decision cycle.

Literature Cited

CUSHING, D. H. 1974. The natural regulation of fish populations. Pages 399–412 in F. R. Harden Jones, ed. Sea fisheries research. John Wiley and Sons, New York.

HOLDEN, M. J. 1974. Problems in the rational exploitation of elasmobranch populations and some suggested solutions. Pages 117–137 in F. R. Harden Jones, ed. Sea fisheries research. John Wiley and Sons, New York.

SCHAEFER, M. B. 1972. Some effects of abiotic environmental factors and of interactions among species on marine fisheries. Pages 53–58 in Progress in fishery and food science. Univ. of Wash. Publ. in Fisheries, New Series, Vol. 5.

National Oceanic and Atmospheric Administration, National Marine Fisheries Service, Washington, D.C. 20235

An Economic View of Optimum Sustainable Yield

James A. Crutchfield

It is with some sadness and a good deal of wonder that I approach my assignment today: sadness that the tremendous accomplishments of fishery scientists, extending over many decades but particularly marked in the past ten or fifteen years, should have produced such limited results in the important arena of public policy; and wonder that all those years of productive research work should have been undertaken without any really general agreement on the objectives to be served. Some years ago a distinguished colleague at the University of Washington, himself a nationally famous fishery scientist, could point to only a handful of fishery management programs in which the real, underlying objectives of management could be related to conservation in any sense—biological, economic, social or any other. Instead, most of the programs seemed to reflect the accumulated effects of successive, piecemeal retreats from sound management in the face of pressure from one group of fishermen, processors, or users, against another group.

It cannot be argued, of course, that fishery scientists are unaware of the confusion about objectives (and, inevitably, the means of achieving them) in framing management programs. But the best that we have been able to do to date seems to be a shift from maximum sustainable physical yield—a concept that ceased to be operational in any useful sense no later than the publication of the first major Beverton-Holt work—to a grudging acceptance of the term optimal sustainable yield by a few scientists and management people with uneasy consciences. But this is only a tiny step forward. Until the term "optimal" is given specific content it represents no more than lip service to the now apparent fact that the human welfare goals of fishery management cannot be fully or even partially served by adhering to the goal of maximum sustainable yield (MSY).

The natural resource economist has something to contribute to the fleshing out of the concept of optimal sustainable yield as an objective function for fisheries management: the economic aspects of the objectives of management; quantifying trade-offs among multiple objectives; the role of cost analysis in assessing alternative ways of achieving given objective sets; and finally some comments on the overwhelmingly important issue of distribution of costs and benefits—who gets the swag and who decides whether or not new entrants are to be entertained.

Maximum physical yield is not an operational objective, and can be seriously misleading as a guide to policy in the common cases with which the fishery manager normally deals. If maximum sustained physical yield really means maximum output of some physical unit (e.g. weight or calories) then the marginal physical product (that is, the incremental addition to output) must be equal for all alternative distributions of the labor and capital employed in fishing effort. In this sense the proposition reduces to an absurdity very quickly. There can be no doubt that we could redistribute capital and labor from the halibut and salmon fisheries of the Northwest and the world tuna fisheries and, with the same inputs, produce far greater quantities of edible food—directly or via conversion into oil and meal and hence into other animal food products. But this, surely, is as nonsensical as asking how much output of edible material could be obtained from the land mass of the United States. If people do not want some of the output, will not eat it, and would cheerfully give up larger quantities of the undesired though edible material for smaller quantities of something which appeals to their tastes and preferences, then maximization of calories from the land area or from the sea makes absolutely no sense in terms of human well being.

If MSY is interpreted to mean maximization of the yield of "desired" species, we have simply substituted an improperly specified economic objective for the ostensibly pristine physical goal of maximizing output.

What is at issue is of profound importance to rational exploitation of living marine resources. No maximization concept geared solely to the output of fish can have any significance in a world in which the real issue is the balancing of more fish against more of the variety of other things that could be produced with the same inputs. In this important sense, optimal utilization of fishery resources, like optimal utilization of any other natural resource, cannot be divorced from optimal utilization of all inputs—natural resources, capital, labor, and technological knowledge—in meeting the multitude of competing demands for all goods and services.

The logical corollary of this argument is that a rational society must be as concerned with the way any given yield from a fish stock is taken as with the level of that yield. In more general terms, the sub-objective with respect to fisheries utilization must be to take any given catch (forgetting for the moment how that catch was determined) at the lowest possible cost in terms of other inputs—a cost which reflects, if the coin is turned over, the value of the other things that could have been produced with those same factors of production.

Resource economists have contributed significantly to at least potential improvement in both utilization and management of fisheries by insisting that management must assess the alternatives available to it with some eye to cost minimization, and, no less important, that management enlist the individual self-interest of harvesters and processers of fishery products in ways that will push them in the direction of greater economic efficiency in their operations. They have also stressed the stultifying effect of management concepts and techniques geared to maximizing physical yield alone in economic improvement. Efficient management of any natural resource must allow for and encourage progressiveness; incentives for research, development, and innovation and the opportunity to utilize these improvements must be built into the regulatory process. Otherwise, as we have seen all too frequently, the initial economic gains from a given fishery management program will inevitably fade away if protection of the stocks can only be achieved by locking the industry into a set of technologies which become more and more outmoded as time goes by.

On the other hand, the concentration of some fishery economists on maximization models has made it needlessly difficult to communicate effectively with either fishery scientists or policy makers in fishery management. In particular, the tendency to model natural resource management problems without regard to the inherent instability of the basic processes underlying the critical yield-effort function can easily give rise to both concepts of maximum net economic yield and techniques for realizing it that are clearly at odds with the reality of resource harvesting and management. From the standpoint of both fishery science and efficient economic utilization of fish stocks, the more interesting problems relate to the quantification of physical yield-effort functions in the more important fisheries subject to management, to the development of causal models that will permit us to trace with reasonable accuracy the time path of adjustments to shifts in parameters, and to analysis of variances in the biometric models and their significance for economic planning by harvesters and for management of their activities by public agencies.

Reasonable data to answer these questions exist for only a handful of fisheries. While one might well plead the inherent complexity of the issues as an obstacle to better quantification, the fact remains that only a small portion of the total fishery research effort is devoted to analysis that would yield answers of greatest use to policy makers concerned with improving the economic performance of managed fisheries.

In short, both the fishery scientist and economist share a common responsibility to pursue, in addition to the more esoteric work at the perimeter of scientific knowledge in their disciplines, a set of more humble tasks designed to move management in the direction of greater net economic benefit, and thus to realize the potential gains in human welfare that the advances in fishery science have made possible. The nearly complete absence of any consideration of economic efficiency in framing fishery management programs and measures means that even fisheries that could be regarded as well managed in a biological sense are simply wasting the potential benefits to humanity through failure to minimize expensive inputs.

Does this view of the urgent need to increase the economic efficiency of fish harvesting operations under management imply that human needs are ignored in the search for greater profit? Clearly not. It must be stressed again and again that economics is essentially a system for choosing among alternatives. Given any desired level of catch and the appropriate information linking various types of fishing effort to output, the economic analyst can specify the least costly way of achieving a given catch level. With some additional information, he may also be able to suggest the right level of total effort and therefore of catch, with proper consideration of the sacrifices in other things that must be made to achieve greater output of fish. Assuming that market mechanisms express, via prices of outputs and inputs, reasonably accurate relative values that society places on different kinds of goods and services, managing a fishery to achieve greater net economic yield means that society can have a greater total output of useful goods and services, and that its inputs will be allocated among competing uses in more efficient fashion. Even when markets function very imperfectly, as may well be the case in many developing nations, economic measures provide at least partial guides to choice among fishing methods and levels of fishing effort.

This is not to say, of course, that economics is the sole technique for choosing among alternative methods of harvesting and managing fishery resources. With respect to fish as with all other natural resources, economics provides a basis for choice resting on efficiency. It is properly regarded as a sub-set of a larger framework for human choice involving other decisions about the distribution of costs and benefits, provision of employment opportunities, changes in the rate and composition of regional economic development, environmental effects, and the like. There is now general agreement among economists concerned with the activities of the public sector that these multiple objectives must be taken into account; the fact that a given fishery management policy may produce a larger economic yield is not always sufficient to make it socially desirable.

It is perfectly plausible, for example, that a given fishery might be managed to maximize net economic returns (and, in the process, assure continued productivity of the stocks in a biological sense) but only by the use of measures which provide such grossly inequitable division of cost and benefits among actual or potential participants as to make it totally unacceptable.

Similarly, it may well be that in some areas (northern Norway, Alaska, and New England come to mind as examples), society may choose to set minimum standards of living in distressed regions where fisheries offer one of the few employment opportunities. Those standards may dictate the use of relatively inefficient harvesting methods as the cheapest of the alternative means of providing a minimum standard of living for the area. This argument is so often abused, however, that I hesitate to offer it as a legitimate one. More often than not, the case for inefficient fishery operations to provide greater employment opportunities is simply a lazy way out of assuming responsibility for what is essentially a regional problem: chronic underemployment and inability of the residents of the area involved to acquire the skills and/or financing to move to areas of greater opportunity. But the fact remains that there are legitimate cases where a careful assessment of all such alternatives leads to the conclusion that inefficient utilization of the fishery resource still provides a social situation more desirable than any other alternative. All the economist can ask is that this be a finding, not an *ex ante* declaration of fact. And he may provide valuable assistance to the ultimate decision-maker in developing estimates of the cost of meeting various minimum levels of employment.

In some respects, the proponents of secondary objectives like employment, income distribution, and other non-efficiency aspects of fishery management have been their own worst enemies. The employment argument, for example, has sufficient legitimacy to make it a matter of real concern in an area like Alaska. On the other hand, the usefulness of that point has been substantially blurred by a great deal of unnecessary breast-beating with respect to the hardship that would be created by "mass unemployment" if some of the excessive capacity were to be weeded out of our presently ludicrously over-capitalized fisheries. A study of the salmon fisheries of the Pacific Northwest suggests, for example, that a reduction of 50% in the total amount of gear now employed in harvesting salmon in the State of Washington would reduce the number of people employed by substantially less than the year-to-year changes in employment by the Boeing Corporation, the largest single employer in the State. It is also smaller than the annual fluctuations in federal employment, the second largest single source of jobs in Washington.

The same study also suggested that a large proportion of those engaged in salmon fishing also have other occupations, for which they are well qualified and in which there are unfilled jobs waiting. The trade-off is significant; at a cost of relocating perhaps 2,000 men over a 5- to 10-year period, at least $8 to $10 million dollars annually could be saved. Another study of the economic potential of a fully developed California anchovy fishery indicated that strenuous union opposition to the introduction of drum seines would save some 200 to 300 jobs, at a cost of $3 to $4 million dollars annually in additional harvesting costs.

In short, there simply are not enough people engaged in commercial fishing in most areas to justify the adoption of grossly inefficient fishing and management techniques on the ground that unacceptable unemployment would

be created by a more rational operation of the fishery.

When the focus is shifted to international fisheries, the question of multiple objectives as constraints on fishery management becomes far more significant. As many writers have pointed out, the definition of an economically optimal level and composition of fishing efforts depends not only on physical yield-effort relations but also on the prices of fish and the cost of the labor and capital inputs required. In an international fishery it would be pure happenstance if the markets of the various countries involved placed the same values on the products derived from the fishery—nor could it be expected that relative prices of labor and capital would yield identical cost functions. Typically, international fisheries are shared by nations for whom prices and relative costs are sufficiently different so that no single level or composition of fishing effort would be optimal for any two. In some cases, differences in relative costs of labor and capital inputs may also dictate the use of different types of gear which are physically incompatible in the same fishing area. Thus, even if we were to accept as a dominant objective of fishery management the achievement of the largest net economic benefit, no single set of policies would represent an optimum for all nations. Instead, it would be essential to define the range within which improvement in economic benefits in the fishery could be realized for at least some participants with no nation any worse off.

Non-efficiency constraints become even more serious at the international level. For example, it is not at all unlikely that for some small coastal nations (and some, like Norway and Japan, not so small) fishery products may loom large enough in the nation's exports to make balance of payments considerations a matter of national interest—bordering, in some instances, on national survival. These countries may be inclined to look, perfectly rationally, at gross income from their share of the catch as a more important consideration than net income.

In the same vein, localized unemployment may be a matter of such political importance in a given nation that it cannot be ignored in international negotiations with respect to joint management. Again, gross rather than net economic shares in the fishery may become the dominant consideration if maintenance of employment is a critical political necessity in the country concerned.

I would repeat, with emphasis, that none of these qualifications alter in any significant way the need to establish improvement in the net economic yield the stocks are capable of providing as a major component in the concept of optimal fishery management. There is no rational way in which the merits of maintaining employment, balance of payments, or other special national objectives can be assessed except in terms of the economic sacrifice required of that nation and its cooperating partners in a jointly shared fishery. The discussion does suggest, however, that any international fishery management program, which seeks real world political feasibility, is subject to two sets of constraints. The first is the need to establish some system of national rights in the fishery that will permit each nation to pursue whatever combination of objectives seems appropriate without imposing its own pattern on other participants. Second, the previous history of the fishery may have produced a set of economic distortions so gross that no program of international management aimed at improving the overall economic performance of the harvesting sector can be accepted if there are major uncompensated losers—this despite the ability to demonstrate that the gains of the winners are more than enough to offset the losses of the losers. This constraint may be ameliorated considerably, however, by compensating concessions outside the fisheries field.

One aspect of the economics of fisheries management which has received far less attention than it deserves, at both national and international level, concerns the costs of information. In general, fisheries science, like most other sciences, has tended to operate on the assumption that all knowledge potentially useful in understanding fish stocks, and therefore assisting in their management, is good. Recent developments in simulation of exploited fishery populations suggests that in fisheries,

as well as in virtually every other resources-oriented activity in which public intervention becomes necessary, the funds available for data acquisition and analysis are grossly inadequate and badly allocated. However trite it may sound, it seems necessary to repeat that the immediate objective of data acquisition in a managed fishery is to define and acquire the *minimum* amount of information that will permit most of the benefits of management to be captured on a timely basis. The importance of timeliness in data acquisition and interpretation and its subsequent translation into management decision-making is infinitely greater in the modern setting. The speed, range, and sweep efficiency of modern fishing fleets is so great that serious biological and economic losses can be inflicted long before the trad{tional techniques for acquiring the analytical basis for management can be carried through to completion. The development of modern computer techniques in the analysis of exploited fisheries opens a whole new range of possibilities for data-economizing approaches to the management of exploited fisheries, in which constantly updated models provide a cheap and reliable technique for testing different combinations of management objectives and methods, and, in the process, for defining with considerably greater accuracy the critical information gaps.

Acceptance of economic efficiency as an important element in a multiple objective function also implies some drastic revision of management techniques. There should be no reason at this time to consider regulations deliberately designed to reduce vessel or gear efficiency or to tolerate those which have that effect, intended or not. Since yield functions are specific to types of gear that can be employed and to their areal and temporal distribution, both economic and biological good sense can come together in proscribing further nonsense of this type.

Again, the application of this test of management techniques is more difficult in an international fishery. Given different relative prices of capital and labor (and different levels of technical expertise), different nations will not always agree on a definition of economically efficient methods of regulating catch. One can hope, however, for agreement on elimination of the more blatantly inefficient.

From the viewpoint of the resource economist, a good "second best" program of management that might be considered a reasonable compromise between optimal and workable would include the following features:

1. A high degree of security with respect to protection of the productivity of the stocks concerned. (Witness the several disasters such as the Peruvian anchovy and California sardine fisheries.)

2. An administrative flexibility to meet unanticipated changes in yield functions originating in the biosystem.

3. A reasonably reliable capacity to model both long-run and short-run responses to changes in effort, gear efficiency, et cetera, and statistical capacity to monitor developments in timely fashion.

4. Positive incentives to both private and public fishing enterprises and regulatory authorities to minimize costs for any chosen level of catch and to re-deploy excess capacity efficiently.

5. Some form of transferrable rights to fish—at both national and individual fishing unit levels.

6. An effective control over new entry, but with provision for ready purchase and transfer of existing rights.

Thus far, only commercial utilization of fishery resources has been considered in giving economic meaning to the concept of optimal yield. A very large and rapidly growing part of the socially useful output from exploited fisheries is the product of recreational fishermen.

The incorporation of this fact of life into active programs is not easy—conceptually or in organizational terms. Perhaps the knottiest issue is the absence of common denominators for measuring sport fishing in economic or even physical units. The output of a sport fishery is not fish but fishing—a service that obviously provides utility over and above the meat value of the catch. The corresponding measures are angler days and values of angler days, which can be linked to numbers of fish

only through complex functions relating angler success to effort and satisfaction derived.

For reasons that cannot be elaborated fully in this limited space, no really satisfactory measure of the economic value of sport fishing has yet been devised. Until there is more widespread acceptance and use of fees or prices as a means of allocating access to sport fishing, such numbers are not likely to be forthcoming.

Thus, the problem of allocating between sport and commercial utilization for a number of very important species—salmon, tuna, billfish, striped bass, bluefish, to name a few—must be resolved without the invaluable aid of a common measuring rod for comparison of values at the margin. Yet the decisions must be made via the political process, and they are critical to any sensible reading of the term "optimal yield." The levels of population and fishing mortality that would be optimal for a purely commercial fishery bear little analytical relationship to those which would be optimal in purely recreational usage. It is particularly important to recognize the "optimal yield" must look beyond a particular stock to the range of stocks that may be directly competitive. Not just salmon but herring—not just barracuda and yellowtail but anchovy.

It is not surprising, then, that the allocation of fish catches among anglers and commercials is largely unplanned or based on weighing of political pressures. We can do better—in many cases, by simple rearrangement of fishing times and areas to minimize conflicts. In others, even the crude measures of sport fishing values now available can be translated into a "better than-worse than" comparison for policy purposes.

I suspect, however, that the most convincing evidence of the value of sport fishing—willingness to pay for the privilege—will remain highly unpopular with large influential blocs of anglers. If so, the complex problems of optimal allocation of species attractive to both groups will remain largely in the political arena.

In summary, acceptance of maximum net economic yield as a primary, though not sole, objective for fishery management could lead to a dramatic improvement in the economic performance of the American fisheries, within a reasonably short period of time. And it provides a proper framework—still crude—for inclusion of both recreational and commercial utilization in a decision matrix. Since it would call for a phased reduction in excess fishing capacity, more effective protection of stocks could be expected, and both industry and government might find again the incentive and opportunity to undertake the research and development work required to improve productivity. Even if one takes a less restrictive view of net economic yield and accepts maximum physical production as a sub-objective, reduction of the inputs required to reach that goal would result in a major improvement in the economic well-being of all elements of the fishing industry.

I recognize fully that other elements of "optimal yield" must be regarded as constraints on purely economic goals: employment, instability in yield determinants, legal obstacles, and problems of jurisdiction. But as long as the ultimate meaning of "optimal" relates to the well-being of the men and women who produce, process, market, and consume fish, or catch them for fun, economic efficiency must be a key objective of fishery management.

Department of Economics, University of Washington, Seattle, Washington 98195

Application of Optimum Sustainable Yield Theory to Marine Fisheries

John Radovich

Although the concept of maximum sustainable yield (MSY) has served fisheries science well over the years, it has tended to become an inflexible goal which has permeated the management philosophy of fishery researchers. As a result, the researcher's sensitivity to the needs and wishes of society has become dulled and his awareness of the intricacies of nature has been ignored in favor of the simplicity and positiveness of his methodology. The concept of maximum economic yield (MEY), which has gained popularity in the past decade, has become another rigid goal toward which fishery scientists have gravitated. It replaced MSY as the philosophy which must be "sold" to society despite society's desires.

If fisheries science is guilty, along with other sciences, big government, industry, and engineering, in helping to develop and control society through a mechanistic and scientistic technocracy, as suggested by expressions of the youth of the turbulent 1960's, then perhaps we should reexamine our motives and goals and redirect them through a responsive methodology which is subservient, rather than dominant, to the society of which we are a part.

There are sociological and political reasons which suggest MSY and MEY be replaced with something more responsive to human needs and desires, and biological reasons why MSY and MEY models do not reflect reality. It is the intent of this paper to examine some of these reasons and to suggest modifications in fisheries management strategy which will reduce some of the technical faults and make management more responsive to society's wishes, whatever they may be.

Maximum Sustainable Yield— A Tool or a Goal?

The rationale for a maximum sustainable yield in commercial fisheries stems from attempts to define overfishing (Graham 1956). More recently, popularity and international acceptance of MSY seem to be related to the idea that the ocean provides the solution to the world's protein deficiency and that the humane thing to do is to make the largest catches that can be made without depleting the resources. Experience, however, does not bear out this premise. Protein deficiencies in Peru, for instance, are really not eased appreciably by the world's largest single-species fishery on the anchoveta. As we all know, fish meal resulting from this industry is exported from protein-deficient Peru so that chickens may be produced much more cheaply for the protein-rich countries of United States and West Germany. The economic benefit realized by Peru has done little to alleviate the protein deficiency of those most in need of protein.

A good case can be made not to harvest at the maximum sustainable yield until the problems of protein distribution can be worked out so that any gain made, while reducing the fish population to the maximum sustainable yield level, can go where it is needed most. Furthermore, it is becoming more and more apparent that the capacity of the ocean to produce protein is limited, that improved agricultural practices may have more promise than the ocean in producing more food, and that the ultimate salvation from protein starvation is human population control.

In addition, in protein-rich nations, particularly the United States, there is growing concern that "quality of life" may best be maintained by leaving some resources completely alone or at least by only partially utilizing them. From this viewpoint, there is really no compelling reason to utilize all the resources to the hilt.

Maximum Sustainable Yield and Sport Fishing

Sport fishermen and some commercial fishermen speak of the "good old days." Many of us may have experienced the "good old days" when we caught fish in relatively virgin waters as fast as we could bait our hooks. Such superlative fishing success is why sportsmen, who can afford to, hire guides to take them on expensive trips into very remote areas. We may define "good old days" as some time and place in the past where fishing was much more productive and hence more satisfying than today.

It has been suggested (McHugh 1966; Radovich 1973) that the interests of sport fishermen may best be served if the resource is at maximum abundance while, internationally, the stated goal almost always is a maximum sustainable yield.

In achieving the maximum sustainable yield, the population level will be reduced substantially from the virgin condition. A sport fisherman, fishing on this resource, will find that his catch-per-unit-of-effort is substantially less, and that there are fewer large trophy fish in his catch, than at some other time in the past.

Since under the stress of high population density, growth rate and maturation tend to slow up and mortality tends to increase, it is likely that the catch-per-effort of the angler may not be linearly related to population size. One might even expect that in a high population density, a fish would strike a lure or bait more readily than it would if it were in a lower population density. This may explain why, off southern California, an expertly presented live bait may only occasionally entice a yellowtail (*Seriola dorsalis*) to bite, while at the 14 fathom spot on Uncle Sam Bank off southern Baja California, even with dead bait, it is difficult to keep yellowtail off your hook while trying to get down through them to the groupers (*Mycteroperca* spp.) and giant sea bass (*Stereolepis gigas*) below. It may also explain why barred sand bass (*Paralabrax nebulifer*) off central Baja California can be taken on bare hooks, while off southern California, where the population is less dense, the catches are relatively difficult to make.

There is even a possibility that a density threshold may exist for some species below which fish may not bite aggressively and above which they will. Shortly after stocking the Salton Sea, and after the initial population explosion of the small bairdiella (*Bairdiella icistia*), not a single orangemouth corvina (*Cynoscion xanthulus*) had been caught in the Salton Sea, even though considerable angling effort had been expended for this species following an announcement by the California Department of Fish and Game that the orangemouth corvina population had reached in excess of 20,000. The next generation of corvina produced a substantial fishery, as have subsequent generations.

I do not mean to imply that population density of the fish stocks is the only factor which influences angling success, but there is considerable evidence that it is a factor. On the other hand, even in heavily fished stocks, for some inexplicable reason, fishing can be exceptional on an occasional day. It is this exceptional day that keeps a large number of anglers fishing. If there were no hope for that exceptional day, angling pressure would not be of the magnitude that it is today; nor would commercial fishing pressure, for that matter.

More efficient gear fished on the same species and in the same area as less efficient gear may cause catches by less efficient gear to decline to a point where the catches are not satisfactory. This may be compounded where the inefficient gear is a hook-and-line fishery and dependent upon the fish's inclination to take the bait, and where that inclination is density dependent. In such a case, as the stock departs from its virgin level, we might even expect the catch-per-angler to drop off more rapidly than the fish population. To the extent that this is true, it would be desirable to maintain a sportfish stock at a population level well above the maximum sustainable level to insure sufficient density of the fish to provide "satisfactory" sport.

Inherent Deficiencies in Some MSY Models

In addition to the problems of using the maximum sustainable yield in the sport fishery, the weakness in the rationale based on feeding the world, and the growing concern in the United States that something less than full utilization may provide the highest quality of life, there are other reasons why maximum sustainable yield may be a weak goal to follow, even for commercial fisheries. First, there is a question of whether the simple "sigmoid" curve of Graham (1948), transformed by Schaefer (1954) to a simple parabola, best defines the maximum sustainable yield or whether the eumetric curve of Beverton and Holt (1957) is a more accurate representation of the real situation. If we prefer the General Production Model of Pella and Tomlinson (1969), the question becomes "which of the family of curves best approximates reality."

Let us assume that we choose the simplest of these representations—the Schaefer model —in which a maximum equilibrium catch exists midway between zero effort, where the population reaches a theoretical limit and the equilibrium catch is zero, and a point on the effort scale where the effort is sufficiently large to reduce the population and equilibrium catch to zero (Figure 1). In most fisheries, sufficient data are lacking to determine where that maximum is and, in some, even whether it exists.

In choosing the model in which the "equilibrium catch" is plotted against fishing effort, an assumption is made tacitly or explicitly that a unit of fishing effort catches a constant proportion of the fishable population. This theoretical unit of effort has been referred to as "real" or "true" fishing effort. The main problem with using the model in this form is that "real fishing effort" exists only in the model. The effort that fisheries

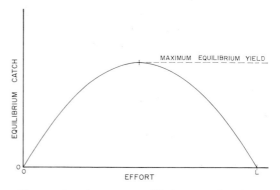

FIGURE 1. Average equilibrium catch plotted against effort, with the maximum equilibrium catch (MSY) occurring midway between zero effort and a limiting effort where the population and catch are driven down to zero.

people generally use, such as a day's fishing, an hour's fishing, the set of a purse seine, or length of a standard drag, is referred to by dynamicists as "nominal fishing effort." "Nominal fishing effort" ultimately relates in some way to effort expended by man. Since fish do not distribute themselves randomly throughout the fishing area, since fishermen do not fish randomly throughout the fishing area, and since "nominal" effort units are not independent (either in time or in space), a "nominal unit of fishing effort" in most cases will not take a constant proportion of the total population. Instead, the efficiency of a unit of effort, insofar as it relates to the proportion of the population that it takes, increases continuously as the population declines.

At extremely large populations, catches tend to saturate gear so that differences in population levels cannot be detected at levels above gear saturation. Limited plant capacities have a similar effect. Many species of fish tend to cluster in school groups in certain areas more often than in others. Since fishermen learn by their experience and communicate with each other, they search where their experience and communication reveal fish are more apt to be found. At lower population levels, the ship's radio becomes more important in assisting communication among fishermen. An entire fleet may become alerted to where fish are concentrated and converge on groups of schools. Under these conditions, fishermen's catches are better than if they had fished independently and searched randomly for fish which were randomly distributed. A high mobility of fishing effort within the fishing area also increases this bias.

At still lower stock sizes, the dependence on communication, radios, and echo sounders increases and eventually, in some fisheries, airplanes are used to locate fish and help fishermen set their nets around schools. All of these factors tend to increase, continuously, the proportion of the fish population taken by a unit of gear as the population declines. As the population increases, the use of airplanes is usually discontinued first and dependence on communication decreases. At higher population levels, radio communication becomes more of a social device than an economic necessity. Fishermen are interested in maximizing their profits, therefore they fish in areas where their probability for success is the greatest.

The bias, which is the result of these factors, causes the "catchability coefficient" to increase continuously as the population declines. Therefore, a fish population which is overfished by too great an expenditure of "nominal effort" should not come to an equilibrium at that effort level, as Schaefer's model predicts (Schaefer 1957), but it should continue to decline until the fishery becomes commercially extinct unless, of course, nominal fishing effort is reduced. Furthermore, at each successively lower population level, effort would have to be reduced to a still lower level in order to start the population to increase. Where year class production is variable, a succession of poor year classes could reduce the population to a level where the "optimum fishing effort" corresponding to the maximum equilibrium catch in Schaefer's model would be sufficient to drive the fishery to commercial extinction unless, of course, some superabundant year classes came along to alleviate this situation.

In fisheries which cover a vast range, where an effort unit cannot reach more than a small part of the range in a day, the increase in efficiency of a unit of effort in a declining fish population would be somewhat less than

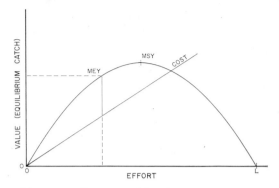

FIGURE 2. Economic yield plotted against effort. Maximum economic yield occurs where the difference between value of the catch and cost of effort is at a maximum. It occurs at a lower effort and, therefore, a higher population size than does MSY.

in a fishery where a fishing vessel is able to land fish from any part of the fishing area the same day as caught. The increase in efficiency in a declining population would be less in the California-based tropical tuna fishery, for example, than in the California sardine (*Sardinops sagax*) fishery. In a trawl fishery, where the unit of gear catches a percentage of what is in the swath and where the catch-per-standard-drag can be integrated over the total area of the fishing grounds, these effects would be somewhat less unless, of course, the fish tended to concentrate.

Problems With Maximum Economic Yield

Since the commonly depicted "maximum economic yield" model is based upon a maximum equilibrium yield model, and merely superimposes "cost" on the "effort" coordinate and "value" on the "equilibrium catch" coordinate, it suffers from exactly the same problem, namely, that the efficiency of a unit of effort increases as the fish population declines (Figure 2). Since the goal of this MEY model is to hold effort at the point which will maximize the difference between the cost of the effort and the value of the yield, a series of poor year classes could reduce the population to a lower level where the efficiency of effort is higher which, in turn, further reduces the population, ad infinitum, until the population is commercially extinct.

The attractive part of using the maximum economic yield is that it occurs at a higher population level than that giving a maximum equilibrium yield. It is this property which has given rise to its popularity. It also may allow some subjective values of the sportsmen's catch to be inserted in the model.

A major part of this problem can be alleviated by using Schaefer's model in a different form, where average equilibrium catch is plotted against population size (Figure 3). In this form, although the inputs may be calculated from similar commercial fisheries data and suffer similar biases, the inferred management strategy is not dependent on holding effort constant, but on varying the catch quota to maintain the population at a size which under average conditions will result in producing the highest average yield. This is a sounder biological approach, but it is unattractive to economists since it does not allow establishment of uniform effort.

Value of a Day's Fishing

In attempting to evaluate sportfishing, some ingenious attempts have resulted in some rather ridiculous answers. There have been numerous attempts, for instance, at trying to determine the value of an "angler-day's fishing." In some cases these are based on the cost of the angler's fishing tackle, gasoline used, price of his boat, outboard motor, food, lodging, and extra beer. Other studies have based the value of an "angler-day's fishing" on the number of miles traveled to reach the fishing area. The results of these studies may equate values for bluegill (*Lepomis macrochirus*) fishing to those for marlin (*Tetrapturus* spp.) fishing, or they may give a value for a day's ocean salmon (*Oncorhynchus tshawytscha*) fishing off San Francisco of $7.00, while the day's fare on a partyboat is $12. In addition to these absurd relationships, there is usually no rational basis for comparing the value of a day's fishing by anglers with a day's fishing by commercial fishermen.

One method which has a number of faults and is generally unacceptable to most economists tends to overcome some of these problems. In a sense, it is a simplified look at

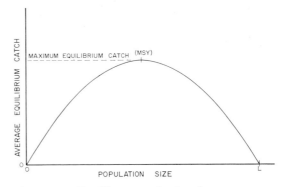

FIGURE 3. Equilibrium catch plotted against population size with the MSY occurring midway between zero population size and a limiting population size.

opportunity costs of anglers and is based on the average daily salary of an individual who happens to be fishing. The rationale for this approach is that an individual chooses to fish on a particular day, instead of working, and that the value to him of his day's fishing should be equal to what he would earn if he had worked. Thus, a day's fishing by the average marlin angler would be worth considerably more than a day's fishing by an average bluegill angler, and this all seems quite logical. Secondly, one can make a comparison directly with a commercial fisherman's day of fishing. He chooses to fish on that day instead of doing something else. Therefore, the value to him of a day's fishing is equal to what he earns for an average day of work. Thus, a direct comparison can be made between anglers and commercial fishermen. However, one needs to determine the value of a day's fishing by a retired person, whether he be a millionaire or a Social Security pensioner, and the value of a day's fishing by children or unemployed housewives. Despite these and other obvious faults, the relative values one gets for a day's fishing for various species will fall into an order that seems quite reasonable to anyone acquainted with these fisheries.

A recent paper by Bryan (1974) suggests that the majority of anglers went fishing to seek satisfaction unrelated to the catching or eating of fish, and that "fisheries managers who concentrate their energies exclusively on the supply of fish can be said to be managing fish production, but they will certainly not be managing sportfish recreation." I have reservations about the conclusions of the study or generalizations that might be made from it but it certainly gives food for thought. Presumably, these approaches, which attempt to place a value on a day's fishing, are aimed at maximizing angler days, or effort, or improving some intangible quality of an angling day which may even involve something not related to the size of the fish population.

Other Problems of Population Parameter Estimations

With all of the faults of the concept of maximum sustainable yield, it is definable. Everyone can know what you are talking about even though it may not really exist. The same thing may be said about an economic yield model based on an equilibrium catch model.

Other methods of estimating parameters of populations or population sizes require different assumptions, most of which also are not met in the ocean. Murphy's (1966) method, for instance, consists of setting up a series of equations, ending up with two more unknowns than equations, and approximating a solution by successive iterations. In order to reduce the number of unknowns to only two more than the number of equations, certain assumptions must be made, such as that a good approximation exists for natural mortality and for the size of a population in one year. Another vital assumption, that natural mortality is constant, is required. Then with a series of equations, each representing a given year and linked to the previous and following year, an iterative solution can be found. The main problems with this approach are that natural mortality does not appear to be a constant in many fisheries—in fact, it may be quite variable (Radovich 1952)— and since the series of equations are linked, estimates of population for each year are affected by all the previous errors. This makes the outcome somewhat dubious. Also, it is difficult to get an initial value for the natural mortality or for the population. If one had a value for natural mortality, and if it were

constant, and if one did know the population size in a given year, of course the system would be quite good provided the fishery was a closed system.

Most models assume either an equilibrium condition or an average condition. Unfortunately, recruitment varies considerably with many species. Recruitment may even be related to distribution. Work done by personnel of the California Cooperative Oceanic Fisheries Investigations suggests that survival may be patchy and that a large year class may be a result of an extremely high survival in a few small areas, while most of the spawn occurring throughout the general spawning area might be doomed to expire.

Although variations in natural mortality and recruitment and the increase in efficiency of a nominal unit of fishing effort seriously limit the use of commercial fisheries data in estimating population parameters, some of these objections can be overcome by using a survey independent of the fishery. Such surveys are expensive, and the relatively smaller effort which can be generated results in greater variability; however, since they can be conducted in a statistically valid manner, they will not have the bias inherent in commercial fisheries data.

Sustaining an Optimum Population Size

Despite all the faults connected with using maximum sustainable yield, ultimately we come back to the problem of having to determine some sort of relationship between the stock size and what it can produce. This appears to be essential except for obvious management situations such as regulating the size of the individual fish caught, as is done with the kelp bass (*Paralabrax clathratus*) in California. Aside from these and similar situations, we are usually faced with determining the amount of fish that can be taken in order to keep the population at a level which will give some kind of a satisfactory yield.

If we can determine the relationship between stock sizes and recruitment, we can use another management strategy which, instead of being sustained, can be quite variable and can be adjusted from year to year as year class survival fluctuates. This requires estimating the annual replacement yield. This value for a given year, according to Gulland and Boerema (in press) ". . . is the catch which, if taken, will leave the abundance of the exploitable part of the population at the end of the year the same as at the beginning. This is specific to a particular year, and includes no concept of continuity. Even if the replacement yield is taken in one year, it is unlikely that the replacement yield in the following year will be the same, unless the population has remained at around the same abundance for some time."

By catching less than the replacement yield, the population will increase, and by catching more, it will decline. The replacement yield can be defined annually, and the quota can be set so that the population can be managed toward any level consistent with what is needed to produce whatever mix of satisfactory yields or satisfactory catches-per-effort is desirable. To do this requires that we must be able to estimate the amount of fish that will be recruited early enough before their recruitment to the fishery to allow us to set quotas. In some fisheries, recruitment may be predicted through the use of independent surveys.

In most cases, the sport fishery takes only a small amount in relation to the commercial fishery. In these cases, the sport fish catch may be estimated and the balance of the quota may be assigned to the commercial fishery. In cases where the sport fishery takes a large proportion of the total catch and is capable of overfishing the stock, other schemes must be devised, such as bag limits and seasons.

Summary

Even though maximum sustainable yield can be precisely defined, for a number of reasons, which have been given, it may be quite meaningless in many ocean fisheries. Maximum economic yield has an advantage over maximum sustainable yield in that it occurs at a larger population size. This gives a greater protection against the possibility of overfishing, but it suffers from most of the inadequacies of maximum sustainable yield since it usually superimposes economic values over a maximum sustainable yield model. Despite the faults of both of these concepts, they can be precisely defined.

Optimum sustainable yield, on the other hand, has no precise definition. It must be arrived at by some subjective decision, usually involving sociological and emotional concepts. "Quality of life," for instance, cannot be defined by logical positivism in a purposive rational manner. "Satisfactory sport" may not be empirically definable either.

I would suggest, therefore, that the term "optimum sustainable yield" be de-emphasized along with maximum sustainable yield and maximum economic yield, since the yield in most cases would be anything but sustainable, and replace it with the concept of managing on the basis of sustaining an "optimum population size." The "optimum population size" would be that size necessary to produce satisfactory fishing success. The concepts of "satisfactory fishing success" as well as "optimum population size," of necessity, must be arrived at subjectively. These values must be responsive to the needs and feelings of society and, therefore, they must be subject to change over time.

Literature Cited

BEVERTON, R. J. H., AND S. J. HOLT. 1957. On the dynamics of exploited fish populations. Min. Agric. Fish. and Food, Fish. Invest., 19(ser. 2): 1–533.

BRYAN, R. C. 1974. The dimensions of a salt-water sport fishing trip or what do people look for in a fishing trip besides fish? Environment Canada, Fish. and Mar. Serv., So. Oper. Br., Pac. Reg. PAC/T-74-1. 35 pp.

GRAHAM, M. 1948. Rational fishing of the cod of the North Sea. The Buckland Lectures for 1939. Edward Arnold and Co., London. 111 pp.

———. 1956. Science and the British fisheries. Pages 1–9 in M. Graham, ed. Sea fisheries: their investigation in the United Kingdom. Edward Arnold (Pub.) Ltd. 487 pp.

GULLAND, J. A., and L. K. BOEREMA. In press. Scientific advice on catch levels. Nat. Mar. Fish. Serv., Fish. Bull.

McHUGH, J. L. 1966. Management of estuarine fisheries. Pages 133–154 in R. F. Smith, A. H. Swartz and W. H. Massmann, eds. A symposium on estuarine fisheries. Spec. Pub. No. 3, Amer. Fish. Soc., Washington, D. C.

MURPHY, G. I. 1966. Population biology of the Pacific sardine (*Sardinops caerulea*). Proc. Calif. Acad. Sci. 34(1): 1–84.

PELLA, J. J., and P. K. TOMLINSON. 1969. A generalized stock production model. Inter-Amer. Trop. Tuna Comm. Bull. 13(3): 421–458.

RADOVICH, J. 1952. Report on the young sardine, *Sardinops caerulea*, survey in California and Mexican waters, 1950 and 1951. Pages 31–63 *in* J. B. Phillips and J. Radovich. Surveys through 1951 of the distribution and abundance of young sardines (*Sardinops caerulea*). Calif. Dept. Fish and Game, Fish Bull. 87.

———. 1973. Letter to the Sport Fishing Institute. *In* Robert G. Martin, Some observations on sustained yield in the sport fisheries. Sport Fish. Inst. Items for Fish. Sci., Jan.-Feb. 1973. [App. to SFI Bull. (241)].

SCHAEFER, M. B. 1954. Some aspects of the dynamics of populations important to the management of the commercial marine fisheries. Inter-Amer. Trop. Tuna Comm. Bull. 1(2): 26–56.

———. 1957. A study of the dynamics of the fishery for yellowfin tuna in the Eastern Tropical Pacific Ocean. Inter-Amer. Trop. Tuna Comm. Bull. 2(6): 247–285.

Operations Research Branch, California Department of Fish and Game, Sacramento, California 95814

Optimum Sustainable Yield in Inland Recreational Fisheries Management[1]

Richard O. Anderson

It is difficult to view current events in a historical perspective, but I believe the topic of this symposium is evidence for the evolution of a new era in fisheries management. For inland fisheries, I denote 1968 as the beginning of an era of effective fisheries management, i.e., management to approach optimum sustainable yield (OSY) with a favorable benefit-cost ratio.

One of the promoters of the new era is Dr. James T. McFadden. His keynote address to the American Fisheries Society in 1968 raised basic and significant questions: What are our objectives in freshwater sport fisheries? How do we optimize yield? (McFadden 1969).

In this paper I explore optimization of the social values in sport fishing. I also develop concepts of form in ecosystems, fish communities, and populations that relate to management for OSY, and present a few programs which have exemplified or may prove to be effective fisheries management for inland recreational fisheries.

Definitions and Concepts

Optimum sustainable yield is a new concept and philosophy for management. We've carried the flag of maximum sustainable yield for quite a while. In practical planning and actual execution the objective usually has been maximum harvest. In sport fisheries management, the number harvested has normally been of primary concern. The philosophy has been more is better. Optimum, in contrast, implies relationships that ascend to an optimum level and then decline.

Yield and harvest are commonly used as synonyms. However, yield in a broad sense implies all benefits to society. The yield of angling includes more than the numbers and weight of fish caught or harvested. It is important also to include dollars as yield. As biologists we tend to overlook the fact that inland sport fishing generated expenditures of about $3.7 billion in 1970 (United States Department of the Interior 1972). The yield or benefits of fishing also include personal gratification and memories. These values, although intangible, are real—and for many anglers are the most significant aspect of yield. It is particularly important to distinguish between the terms catch, harvest, and yield in a recreational fishery. Under restrictive regulations, trout or bass that are caught and released contribute nothing to harvest but do contribute to the quality of fishing and memories, and therefore have yield value.

Optimization of yield is a more challenging and demanding goal than maximization of harvest. Optimum is defined as most favorable, with many factors to be considered. In both commercial and sport fisheries, the factors are biological, social, and economic. In reality, achievement of the optimum is an idealistic dream. Optimum yields for fisheries management are not constant either within or between ecosystems because of the dynamic and variable nature of aquatic ecosystems, fish populations, and public values. In contrast to commercial fisheries and fish farming where optimum yield is related to net return or profit, optimum yield in sport fishing is related to the quality of fishing. A sustained satisfactory quality of fishing is necessary if

[1] Contribution from the Missouri Cooperative Fishery Research Unit, a cooperative program of the United States Fish and Wildlife Service, the University of Missouri, and the Missouri Department of Conservation.

we are to approach optimum sustainable economic and social benefits. Effective management will sustain satisfactory yields or provide better sustainable yields that are closer to an optimum value.

Sustainable implies that some period of time should be considered in formulating management objectives. A put-and-take fishery must consider short-term or week to week variation. Sport fisheries dependent on natural production must consider year to year variation, as well as long-term averages. Management objectives could be set not only for average values but also for the range over time intervals.

Managers must develop formal objectives in order to achieve effective fisheries management and to approach optimum sustainable yield. "Soft" objectives such as wise use or providing fishing opportunities cannot be a basis for evaluating management effectiveness (Lackey 1974).

Factors Affecting Optimum Sustainable Yield

Social Values

Fishing quality means different things to different people. There is no average fisherman. Personal values vary over time as an individual evolves from a novice fisherman to a piscatorial expert to a philosophical angler. An individual's values also depend on where and for what species he is fishing. Socially successful management provides a variety of recreational fisheries to create an opportunity for choice. Administration of variable programs and objectives may be complex, but optimum yield involves accommodation of people as well as fish.

Management of recreational fisheries can strongly influence the number, size, and species of fish caught and harvested. The size and number of fish caught were the most important values that determined the quality of the fishing experience in a western trout fishery cited by McFadden (1969). In a New York study, however, anglers ranked the importance of size and number of fish caught below that of water quality, natural beauty, and privacy while fishing (Moeller and En-

gelken 1972). However, a fisherman asked about his most memorable fishing trip will probably recall an individual large fish or a particularly good catch. A problem to fisheries managers lies in the fact that fishing is an individual experience. The measure of quality to the individual is personal success and gratification. The quality of fishing and the number and size of fish caught may be much better in private waters or where effort is lower than in heavily fished public waters. The concept of limited entry in commercial fisheries has only limited application for sustaining recreational fishing quality in the management of public waters in North America. Since effort is a variable over which management normally has little direct control, the potential quality of fishing and the proximity to optimum catch, harvest, and yield in most waters will be determined by the form (e.g., standing crop, biomass ratios, length-frequency distribution) and rate functions (e.g., recruitment, growth, mortality) of aquatic organisms.

Production in Aquatic Ecosystems

The holistic view of aquatic ecosystems is an important part of the science that contributes to the art of management. I believe fishery biologists should think of aquatic ecosystems as successive levels of production (tissue elaboration). Even though limnologists and theoretical ecologists will strongly disagree with the semantics, I contend that the primary level of production of greatest significance to society in aquatic ecosystems is made up of various fish species—not phytoplankton. The primary level of production may consist of rainbow trout (*Salmo gairdneri*) or coho salmon (*Oncorhynchus kisutch*) in cold waters, or largemouth bass (*Micropterus salmoides*) in warm waters. The secondary level consists of the organisms which serve as food for the primary level. The organic base for the pyramid of production in an ecosystem is made up of the plant production, allochthonous organic matter, and bacterial production—both autotrophic and heterotrophic.

The capacity for production of fishes in an aquatic ecosystem is related to the size of the organic base and the efficiency of production in successive levels. One way to predict optimum fish harvest may be to quantify the size of the organic base in managed ecosystems. In classical limnology, the productivity of lentic waters ranges from oligotrophic to eutrophic. Eutrophication as used in many recent scientific and popular articles is associated with pollution, and biological and economic death of aquatic ecosystems. This connotation and the "problem" of nutrients were reassessed by Martin (1974). He suggested that in many ecosystems it is not a problem and cited Lake Erie as an example. The trophic state of ecosystems for management purposes should be placed on a scale of hypotrophy–mesotrophy–hypertrophy (Fig. 1). The range of mesotrophy for waters could be defined as a satisfactory state relative to water quality and fishery objectives.

Optimum yield of sport fisheries is not only related to the biomass or production of the organic base but also to qualitative characteristics of the aquatic flora. Management to achieve optimum yield should prevent the development of noxious blooms of bluegreen algae as well as the chronic excessive growth of filamentous algae and aquatic plants.

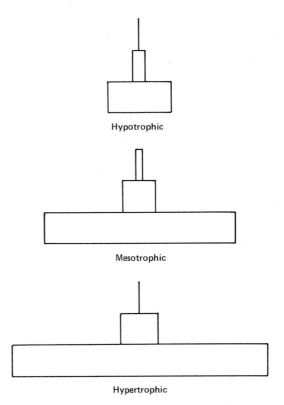

FIGURE 1. Models of low, medium, and high trophic states. The bottom bar of each pyramid represents the size of the organic base for each ecosystem.

Balance of Fish Communities and Populations

The pyramid of production in an aquatic ecosystem or portions of the pyramid representing the fish community can be considered balanced or unbalanced. A balanced fish community has the capacity to provide a satisfactory and sustained harvest of fish of desirable size in proportion to the productive capacity of the system. The term "balance" does not describe a state of static equilibrium; it has an artistic connotation. A balanced fish community or aquatic ecosystem is like a work of art in that critics can be complimentary in their evaluation and response. The state of balance relative to management objectives has a strong influence on how close we can approach optimum sustainable catch, harvest, and yield.

In two similar ponds with the same type and amount of invertebrate forage produc-

tion, there may be markedly different productions of bluegills (*Lepomis macrochirus*) and largemouth bass (Fig. 2). Bluegill populations with excessive numbers of fish of intermediate size may be more efficient in their harvest or consumption of food and may have relatively high production of fish of less than harvestable size. In the absence of effective bass predation, total production of the fish community may provide only a low quality of fishing and have limited potential for harvest and yield. This conceptual model for bass and bluegill may be appropriate for other fish communities such as walleye (*Stizostedion vitrium*) and yellow perch (*Perca flavescens*), and coho salmon and alewives (*Alosa pseudoharengus*).

The form of the different levels of production in fish communities is of theoretical interest and significance. Determination of annual production rates in a fish community is

Pyramid Of Production

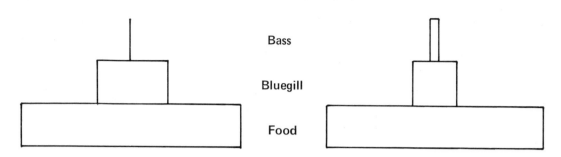

Bass

Bluegill

Food

Pyramid Of Potential Yield

Bass

Bluegill

Unbalanced   **Balanced**

FIGURE 2. Pyramids of production and potential yield of balanced and unbalanced fish communities. The areas of the bars at the same level of production are comparable; areas between levels of production are not to scale.

neither practical nor necessary. For management purposes the state of balance of simple fish communities in ponds consisting of bass and bluegill populations is identified as satisfactory or unsatisfactory on the basis of several characteristics: the relative success of recruitment of young to the populations; biomass ratios between predator and prey; and the proportion of the total weight of fish that are of harvestable size (Swingle 1950, 1956). The state of balance of complex fish communities in large reservoirs or lakes can probably best be assessed by biomass ratios or estimates of the proportion by weight of key species in the total fish community (E Value: Swingle 1950). Key species may be large

predators such as largemouth bass or potentially serious competitors for sport fishes such as carp (*Cyprinus carpio*).

Balance can also refer to the state of a population of a single fish species. A similar definition may apply—the capacity to provide a satisfactory and sustained harvest of fish of desirable size. In order to approach optimum sustainable yield or achieve a satisfactory quality of fishing for a sport fish species, the size distribution of fish in the population is of paramount importance. The functions of reproduction, recruitment, growth, and mortality that determine annual production also determine the form or length-frequency distribution of a population. Johnson and Anderson (1974) suggest that bluegill populations in Missouri ponds may be balanced when numbers of intermediate and adult bluegill have a size distribution of: 75–150 mm (3–5.9 inches), 75%; >150 mm (6 inches), 25%. The suggested size distribution for balanced largemouth bass populations in reservoirs is: 200–299 mm, (8–11.9 inches), 40 to 50%; 300–375 mm (12–14.9 inches), 35 to 40%; >375 mm (15 inches), 10–25%.

Fisheries management must identify problems which are associated with a product of interest. The primary product of interest to short-term management objectives is the population or community which most adversely affects potential yield values and which is amenable to management. The primary product of interest in a pond may be the bluegill population or the community of rooted aquatic plants. Management strategies and tactics can be aimed directly at the product of interest (e.g., selective toxicants, increased harvest), the level of production below the product of interest (e.g., nutrients for plants or food for fish) or the level of production above (i.e., consumer populations).

In management of fish populations and communities it is important to distinguish between symptoms and problems. Symptoms can be seen, whereas problems are caused by some adverse rate of recruitment, growth, or mortality in a population. In the layman's sense, a pond with relatively small, slow growing adult bluegills and a beach piled high with decomposing alewives are problems. In an ecological sense these are symptoms of lack of balance in the fish community. Too often simple management logic has dictated attacking symptoms and reducing densities by means of chemical, angler, or commercial harvest. In order to approach optimum sustainable yield, the economic and social enhancement of resources can often best be achieved by better balance in fish populations and communities.

Effective Fishery Management

Introductions

Introductions, stocking, and regulations are traditional techniques that can play an impor-

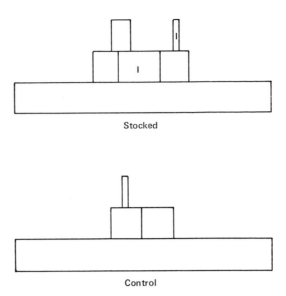

Stocked

Control

FIGURE 3. Changes in ecosystem structure with the introduction of new species (I) at the primary and secondary levels of production.

tant role in effective fisheries management. Introduced species can improve ecological efficiencies and enhance production as an approach to OSY (Fig. 3). Any introduction deserves research and evaluation to determine ecological, social, and economic benefits and costs.

Tody and Tanner (1966) developed the case for introduction of coho salmon in the Great Lakes, a classic example of manipulating fish community structure. The alewife was transformed from a major nuisance to a valuable forage fish. In Michigan waters sport fishing for salmonids expanded from insignificance in 1965 to more than 3 million angler days in 1971; net economic worth surpassed $20 million a year and the benefit-cost ratio exceeded 10:1 (Michigan Department of Natural Resources 1973). The program of introductions has been modified and refined to include rainbow trout, chinook salmon (*Oncorhynchus tshawytscha*), brown trout (*Salmo trutta*) and Atlantic salmon (*Salmo salar*) in several locations.

Many warmwater impoundments have the capacity to produce large piscivorous species. Introductions may be an efficient technique to improve the form of the fish community and the quality of fishing (Anderson 1973). Research is needed to determine what, where, and when introduced species may be effective, and to evaluate benefit-cost relationships.

Introduction of fishes strictly for forage may or may not be effective. Diversity should enhance production and community stability. Introduction of threadfin shad (*Dorosoma petenense*) in southern reservoirs has been considered effective; introduction of gizzard shad and golden shiners (*Notemigonus cryso-leucas*) into a 14-hectare (35-acre) lake along with bluegills apparently enhanced the growth of young largemouth bass (Johnson and Anderson 1974). Other introductions have been less successful: golden shiners alone could not sustain satisfactory bass production in New York ponds (Regier 1963); introduction of a minnow had an adverse effect on trout production in a Canadian lake (Larkin and Smith 1954). The introduction of invertebrate species, which has received considerable attention in the management of Russian ecosystems (Yanushevich 1966), has shown both benefits (increased fish production) and liabilities (some invertebrates are a vehicle for the spread of serious fish parasites). As with large predators, what forage species to introduce and where and when to introduce them are appropriate subjects for research and evaluation.

Introduction of grass carp (*Ctenopharynge-don idella*) to regulate the quantity or quality of aquatic plant production is a controversial issue. Little research has been conducted to evaluate the ecological impact of the species. In short-term studies in experimental ponds with excessive weed growth in Missouri, the addition of grass carp not only changed the trophic state from hypertrophic to mesotrophic, with an associated improvement in water quality (oxygen, pH), but also appeared to have no adverse effect on the production of bluegills and fathead minnows (Roger Rottmann, personal communication). The economics of potential sustained vegetation regulation and manipulation with grass carp are especially attractive when compared with the cost of chemical or mechanical control. If these results are supported by subsequent long-term studies in ponds and lakes with chronic excess growth of plants, the grass carp may prove to be a valuable asset in the approach toward optimum sustainable yield with a favorable benefit-cost ratio.

Stocking

Many trout fisheries are supported by stocking catchable trout. In Missouri, where stream habitat for trout is a unique resource, an effective program has evolved. Four parks with large cold water springs are stocked daily during the fishing season with rainbow trout 25 cm (10 inches) long or longer at a rate of 2.25 fish per fisherman. The stocked streams total 17 hectares (42.5 acres) in area and 9.6 km (6 miles) in length. The program has grown from 27,200 angler-days in 1939, when the daily fee was $0.25, to a high of 385,000 angler days in 1971, when the fee was $1.25. I consider this program an example of effective management for several reasons: (1) opportunities to catch trout are limited in Missouri; (2) the program is a popular form of recreation and most of the fishermen catch fish; (3) more than 90% of the trout stocked are caught; and (4) the cost of the program is borne by the participants. An efficient and effective hatchery program contributes to optimum yield and a favorable benefit-cost ratio.

The future of stocking catchable trout in Colorado streams was examined by Marshall (1974). In a study on the Cache la Poudre River, stocked sections supported three times as much fishing pressure as unstocked "quality waters." An average harvest of 0.4 to 0.5 fish per hour was observed for both sections. The program was a biological success: 85 to nearly 100% of the stocked fish were harvested; resident rainbow and brown trout populations remained similar in stocked and unstocked sections. A case for reduced stocking in the future was based on economic considerations. It was estimated that 70% of all fishing license revenues are required to support the put-and-take stocking program. Marshall concluded that fishermen using low-cost management areas are forced to subsidize high-cost management areas at an annual rate of $169/km ($272/mile).

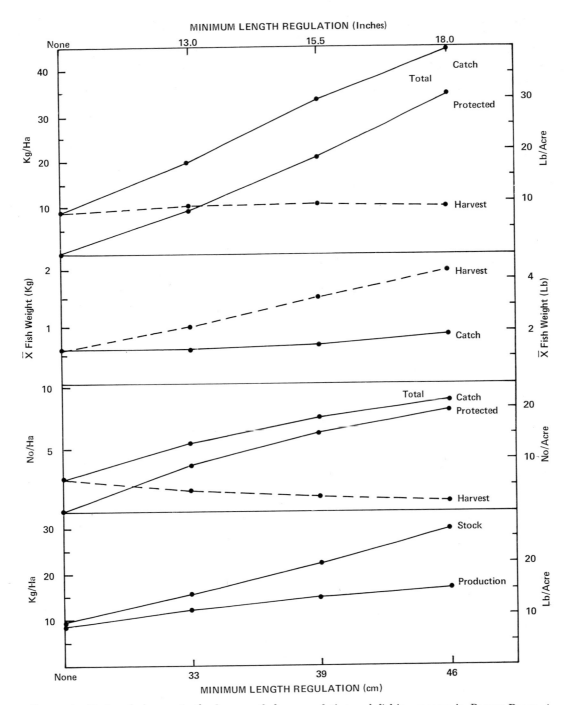

FIGURE 4. Projected changes in the largemouth bass population and fishing success in Beaver Reservoir under different minimum length regulations.

Management of trout in lakes based on stocking and evaluation in California was discussed by Borgeson (1966), who cited examples of effective fisheries management. His reported hatchery cost of $0.33/kg ($0.15/pound) of trout "in the creel" in Crowley Reservoir is certainly a favorable benefit-cost ratio.

Regulations

Effective regulations are a fishery manager's most useful tools for sustaining balance in fish communities and populations. The consumer level above the primary level of production (e.g., largemouth bass) is normally man. Anderson (1974) developed a theoretical response of largemouth bass to various minimum length regulations in Beaver Reservoir. On the basis of data from Bryant and Houser (1971), I estimated the following average population statistics in the absence of a length limit: a stock of 9.6 kg/hectare (8.6 pounds/acre); a low annual recruitment rate for age II of 15 fish/hectare (6/acre); and a high annual mortality rate of 68%. I estimated changes in stock biomass, annual production, potential harvest and catch assuming minimum length limits of 33, 39, and 46 cm (13.0, 15.5, and 18 inches) to protect bass through age II, III, or IV. Annual mortality was assumed to be 30% for protected age groups. Estimated stock biomass increased to 29.6 kg/hectare (26.4 pounds/acre) with the 46-cm (18-inch) length limit (Fig. 4). This value is presumed to be within normal carrying capacity for bass for the reservoir. Estimated numerical harvest was highest with no length limit; a minimum length limit of 39 cm (15.5 inches) was estimated to increase the weight of annual harvest by 20% (1.8 kg/hectare or 1.6 pounds/acre). Estimated total annual number caught improved with higher length limits because of the catch and release of protected bass. The average size caught and harvested increased with length limits. There was a calculated 10-fold increase in the harvest of large bass (1.6 kg, 3.5 pounds, and heavier) with a minimum length limit of 46 cm (18 inches). Of the three length limits, the one presumed to achieve the best quality of fishing (number

caught, weight caught, average size harvested) was 46 cm (18 inches). In theory, increased bass biomass and production may improve fish community balance to benefit yields of crappies (*Pomoxis* sp.) and white bass (*Morone chrysops*). The regulation that will best approach optimum yield depends not only on the response and dynamics of bass and the fish community, but also on the response of anglers.

The potential benefits of high minimum length limits on bass have been indicated on several Missouri waters. The imposition of minimum length limits of 30 to 38 cm (12 to 15 inches) was the only measure effective in preventing overharvest of largemouth bass when new impoundments were first opened to fishing (Redmond 1974).

A 30-cm (12-inch) minimum length limit was established on smallmouth bass on the Big Piney River in 1967; fishing pressure, catch, and harvest were estimated from 1963 to 1972 (Fleener 1974). Statistics before and after the change in regulation include: average annual bass harvest decreased from 3.2 to 2.8 kg/hectare (2.9 to 2.5 pounds/acre); number of bass caught approximately doubled in 1967–1972; average weight of bass harvested increased from 375 g (13.2 ounces) to 588 g (20.7 ounces); average harvest of bass 30 cm (12 inches) or more in length increased from 748/year to 1000/year; average weight of rock bass (*Ambloplites rupestris*) harvested changed from 125 g (4.4 ounces) to 196 g (6.9 ounces); nearly 2000 more rock bass were caught annually in 1967–1972 than in 1963–1966; average size and harvest of green sunfish (*Lepomis cyanellus*), longear sunfish (*Lepomis megalotis*) and bluegills also increased in 1967–1972. The highest number of man-hours of fishing was observed in the last two years of the study. The regulation was considered effective. A statewide 30-cm (12-inch) minimum length limit for bass in Missouri streams was established in 1974.

Satisfactory catch and harvest rates have been sustained on two new Missouri reservoirs where minimum length regulations were applied on largemouth bass—Binder Lake

TABLE 1.—*Angler effort and yield data for two Missouri reservoirs with minimum length regulations on largemouth bass.*

	Area	Opening year	Annual effort	Bass yield Catch (no.)	Bass yield Harvest (no.; wt)	Bluegill harvest (no.; wt)
Binder	61 hectares	1968	692 hr/ha	215/ha	25; 17 kg /ha	820; 93 kg/ha
(1973)	150 acres		280 hr/a	87/a	10; 15.2 lb/a	332; 83 lb/a
Pony Express	97 hectares	1966	1176 hr/ha	193/ha	21; 11.5 kg/ha	682; 69.1 kg/ha
(1968–1972)	240 acres		476 hr/a	78/a	8.4; 10.3 lb/a	276; 61.7 lb/a

(Hoey and Redmond 1974) and Pony Express Lake (Ming and McDannold 1974). Binder Lake was first opened to fishing in September 1968; the minimum length limit on bass has been 36 cm (14 inches). Pony Express Lake was first opened in 1966; a minimum 30-cm (12-inch) length limit on bass was established in 1968. Creel census data were collected at Binder Lake in 1973 and at Pony Express Lake from 1968–1972. Angler effort is considered relatively high (Table 1). The annual catch of bass probably exceeds the number in bass stocks in both lakes. The total weight and average size of bass harvested appear satisfactory; the number and average weight of bluegills harvested appear exceptional for Missouri reservoirs, particularly compared to others without a length limit on bass. The regulations appear to have improved the sustained yield and quality of fishing in these lakes.

The quality of bass fishing was considered less than optimal from 1966 to 1973 on a 14-hectare (35-acre) private lake with a 30-cm (12-inch) minimum length limit on bass (Johnson and Anderson 1974). Few bass longer than 38 cm (15 inches) were collected in electrofishing surveys. Because of normally high annual recruitment, an experimental regulation to protect bass 30–38 cm (12–15 inches) was established in 1974. The management objectives are to harvest a surplus of bass 200–299 mm (8–11.9 inches) long, increase the catch of bass 300–375 mm (12–14.9 inches) long, increase the harvest of bass longer than 375 mm (15 inches), and to sustain the quality of bluegill fishing.

Effective regulations on bass harvest appear to be a primary consideration in approaching optimum sustainable yield and high-quality fishing in warmwater ecosystems. From an economic benefit-cost standpoint, regulations are a relatively low-cost management technique. A central problem for fisheries science and management is to determine what factors influence the optimum length regulation.

The Larger Problem

I have attempted to discuss selected aspects of the optimum sustainable yield concept in freshwater recreational fisheries management. A broader question that needs consideration is optimum yield of aquatic ecosystems. Conservation has long been defined as wise and multiple use. The values of sport fish and fishing must be recognized as only part of the potential social and economic yield of aquatic ecosystems.

The optimum yield concept needs to be applied in a wide range of land use, water development, and water quality decisions. The present national goal relative to water quality is to eliminate the discharge of pollutants. The optimum yield concept would recognize optimum water quality as a concept and goal. In different waters there may be a major difference between the economic cost of the elimination of discharge of pollutants and a goal of optimum water quality. It is to be hoped that the modelers of the near future will have the technical capacity and wisdom to apply the optimization concept to not only water quality but also the quality of life. The objectives are balanced political, social, and economic systems.

I have indicated above that optimum sustainable yield is an idealistic dream. However, I believe the concept of the optimum in the decision making process is like a star to a mariner. You know it is there; you cannot reach it as a goal but it can be used as a guide in setting priorities and objectives.

Literature Cited

ANDERSON, R. O. 1973. Application of theory and research to management of warmwater fish populations. Trans. Amer. Fish. Soc. 102(1) : 164–171.

———. 1974. Problems and solutions, goals and objectives of fishery management. Proc. Southeast. Assoc. Game Fish Comm. 27 (1973) : 391–401.

BORGESON, D. P. 1966. Trout lake management. Pages 168–178 in A. Calhoun, ed. Inland fisheries management. California Department of Fish and Game, Sacramento.

BRYANT, H. E., and A. HOUSER. 1971. Population estimates and growth of largemouth bass in Beaver and Bull Shoals Reservoirs. Pages 349–357 in G. E. Hall, ed. Reservoir fisheries and limnology. Amer. Fish. Soc. Spec. Publ. No. 8, Washington, D.C.

FLEENER, G. G. 1974. Harvest of fish from the Big Piney River. Job completion report. Missouri D.J. Project F-1-R22, Study S-2, Job 1.

HOEY, J. W., and L. C. REDMOND. 1974. Evaluation of opening Binder Lake with a length limit for bass. Pages 100–105 in J. Funk, ed. Symposium on overharvest and management of largemouth bass in small impoundments. North Central Div., Amer. Fish. Soc. Spec. Publ. No. 3.

JOHNSON, D. L., and R. O. ANDERSON. 1974. Evaluation of a 12-inch length limit on largemouth bass in Philips Lake, 1966–1973. Pages 106–113 in J. Funk, ed. Symposium on overharvest and management of largemouth bass in small impoundments. North Central Div., Amer. Fish. Soc., Spec. Publ. No. 3.

LACKEY, R. T. 1974. Priority research in fisheries management. Wildl. Soc. Bull. 2(2) : 63–66.

LARKIN, P. A., and S. B. SMITH. 1954. Some effects of introduction of the redside shiner on the Kamloops trout in Paul Lake, British Columbia. Trans. Amer. Fish. Soc. 83: 161–175.

MARSHALL, T. L. 1974. The fish stocking program —What is its future? Trout 15(3) : 21, 28, 30.

MARTIN, R. G. 1974. Reassessing the eutrophication scare. SFI (Sport Fish. Inst.) Bull. 257: 4–6.

McFADDEN, J. T. 1969. Trends in freshwater sport fisheries in North America. Trans. Amer. Fish. Soc. 98(1) : 136–150.

MICHIGAN DEPARTMENT OF NATURAL RESOURCES. 1973. Michigan's Great Lakes trout and salmon fishery 1969–1972. Fish Manage. Rep. No. 5. 105 pp.

MING, A., and W. McDANNOLD. 1974. Length limit for bass in Pony Express Lake. Final Rep. Missouri D.J. Project F-1-R22, Study I-1, Job 2.

MOELLER, G. H., and J. H. ENGELKEN. 1972. What fishermen look for in a fishing experience. J. Wildl. Manage. 36(4) : 1253–1257.

REDMOND, L. C. 1974. Prevention of overharvest of largemouth bass in Missouri impoundments. Pages 54–68 in J. Funk, ed. Symposium on overharvest and management of largemouth bass in small impoundments. North Central Div., Amer. Fish Soc., Spec. Publ. No. 3.

REGIER, H. A. 1963. Ecology and management of largemouth bass and golden shiners in farm ponds in New York. N.Y. Fish Game J. 10(2) : 139–169.

SWINGLE, H. S. 1950. Relationships and dynamics of balanced and unbalanced fish populations. Auburn Univ. Agric. Exp. Sta., Bull. 274. 74 pp.

———. 1956. Appraisal of methods of fish population study—Part IV. Determination of balance in farm fish ponds. Trans. North Amer. Wildl. Conf. 21: 298–322.

TODY, W. H., and H. A. TANNER. 1966. Coho Salmon for the Great Lakes. Mich. Dep. Conserv., Fish. Manage. Rep. No. 1.

UNITED STATES DEPARTMENT OF THE INTERIOR. 1972. National survey of fishing and hunting 1970. U.S. Fish Wildl. Serv., Resour. Publ. 95. 108 pp.

YANUSHEVICH, A. I., ed. 1966. Acclimatization of animals in the USSR. Israel Prog. Sci. Trans. Ltd., Cat. 1218. Jerusalem.

Cooperative Fishery Research Unit, Stephens Hall, University of Missouri, Columbia, Missouri 65201

Optimum Sustainable Yield—Commercial Fisheries Views

Robert G. Mauermann

The concept of optimum sustainable yield in the management of fisheries resource is not new. The Honorable Maurice H. Stans, Former Secretary of Commerce, in the forward to *Our Changing Fisheries*, U.S. Government Printing Office, Washington, D. C., 1971, said: "The Federal Government is committed to the goal of optimum use of the living resources of the sea. There are many roads to be traveled before we converge at that goal: We need to understand the water environment better and how it relates to communities of aquatic animals. We need to manage the commercial and sport harvest of these resources economically and at their optimum sustainable yield for all time."

Management for optimum sustainable yield of a number of species of fish in small impoundments has been very successfully accomplished by biologists for many years. The principles of optimum sustainable yield developed by scientists like Professor Homer Swingle of the University of Alabama have been applied to small lakes and ponds all over the country, and more recently to the commercial production of catfish in the South. Our capability, however, to manage fisheries resources for optimum sustainable yield in larger bodies of waters decreases as the size of the environment increases until we reach the open oceans of the world, where our scientific knowledge is most limited and the practices of resource utilization by fishermen from the four corners of the world are often in conflict with one another.

Optimum sustainable yield means different things to different people. Webster defines optimum as a noun to mean: The best or most favorable condition for obtaining a given result, or more simply, as we are considering its use today, best or most favorable. To the beginning angler a dozen small sunfish may be the best or most favorable result, whereas to the more seasoned angler a half dozen small trout taken on a deftly cast, handmade fly may well be the most favorable result. To most experienced southern bass fishermen, optimum sustainable yield could well mean a half dozen four- or five-pound bass rather than twenty-five or thirty one-pound bass.

To the various segments of the commercial fishing industry in the United States, optimum sustainable yield also has different meanings. I should like to explore some of these with you today. First, let us examine the nation's most valuable commercial fishery, the Gulf shrimp industry.

The shrimp fishery in the United States has enjoyed unprecedented growth and prosperity during the past twenty years and has been recognized by economists as the nation's most valuable fishery. The most important shrimp producing area of the United States is the Gulf of Mexico, which in 1973 accounted for 182.1 million pounds of the total United States landings of 372.2 million pounds and represented a value of $173.0 million or 79% of the total value ($219.4 million) of all U.S. shrimp landings in 1973.

Prior to 1948, the shrimp industry in the five Gulf states was limited to white shrimp (*Penaeus setiferus*) taken in the bays and estuaries and to a limited extent around passes fairly close inshore in the Gulf. In 1948 the discovery of brown shrimp (*Penaeus aztecus*) in deeper waters of the Gulf itself opened up a new industry. The development of new fishing techniques, freezer equipment, and larger boats capable of ranging the entire

Gulf of Mexico followed. Today there are approximately 4,000 Gulf shrimp trawlers operating in the Gulf, with an estimated total value of 360 million dollars. There are also a great number of small fishing boats which operate on a seasonal basis in the bays. Fishing for shrimp by weekend sports fishermen is particularly popular in Louisiana and the upper Texas coast. Providing sports fishermen with both live and dead shrimp for bait is also an important segment of the shrimp industry in the Gulf of Mexico.

For many years industry leaders and fisheries scientists have recognized the need for a management plan involving all the Gulf states and the Republic of Mexico, not only for shrimp, but for all marine species which have a recreational or commercial value. The Gulf States Marine Fisheries Commission was created primarily for the purpose of coordinating fishing regulations within the five Gulf states. Unfortunately, little progress has been made. Legislation now pending in the federal congress implementing the state-federal management concept will provide the machinery necessary to develop comprehensive management plans for the nation's renewable marine resources.

As a management concept, optimum sustainable yield is not new to the Gulf shrimp industry. In 1959 the Texas legislature, at the request of industry leaders, passed what is now known as the Texas Shrimp Conservation Act. The Act provides for certain closed seasons in the bays, a size limit, a daily catch limit and a 45-day closed season in the Gulf of Mexico out to nine miles from shore. Nowhere in the statute is the term optimum sustainable yield used, yet that is what the Act is all about. The Act is designed to protect small shrimp until they reach an optimum size for harvest, which simply means when the most dollars accrue to the fishermen for the least amount of product and/or effort. The value of shrimp, unlike that of other types of seafood, varies greatly according to animal size. As an example, green headless shrimp under 15 to the pound on today's market are sold at the docks for 3 times as much as 36–40 to the pound.

There are conflicts within the shrimp industry on when and at what size shrimp should be harvested. The bay fisherman, the bait fisherman, the weekend sports shrimper, and the wide-ranging Gulf shrimper all depend on the same resource, but harvest this resource at different stages of its development. Again we see a different meaning of the optimum sustainable yield concept as it relates to the several segments of the shrimp fishery. If we apply optimum sustainable yield as viewed by the Gulf shrimper to the bay operator or the smaller bayou fisherman in Louisiana, they would be out of business. Several million pounds of small shrimp are harvested annually by bay fishermen. If these shrimp were permitted to reach maturity they would move into the Gulf and be unavailable to the bay fishermen. There is also disagreement among biologists about the effect of a heavy annual harvest of immature shrimp in the bays. Some marine biologists maintain that the present level of harvest of small bay shrimp does not materially affect the availability of the resource later in the year in the open Gulf. Others are skeptical, as are the Gulf shrimpers who see tons of tiny "eyeballs and whiskers" taken in the bays and realize that in a few weeks these small shrimp would reach an optimum size for their market and might be available to them.

The fishing industry in Mexico is rapidly expanding. The Mexican Government's plans call for the construction of about 500 new fishing vessels, 300 of which will be shrimp boats. In addition, more than 50 used American shrimp boats have recently been purchased by private interests in Mexico. Shrimp are one of Mexico's major exports. In 1973 Mexico exported 76,105,000 pounds worth $111.0 million to the United States.

The Mexican shrimp industry has suffered some serious problems as a result of overfishing their shrimp resources, both in the Pacific and in the Gulf of Mexico. For the first time, fisheries authorities in Mexico closed all Mexican waters for a 45-day period this past summer to permit small shrimp to reach a more valuable size. We congratulate Mexico for taking a giant step forward in the management of her most valuable renewable marine resource. Thus, we see our neighbors to the south applying the principle of optimum sustainable yield to at least one important commercial marine species.

Although total landings of shrimp in the Gulf of Mexico have steadily increased, the landings per boat have decreased, which, of course, has resulted in an increased cost of production per pound of shrimp and a decrease in the margin of profit for the fisherman. The only solutions are higher prices for shrimp and increased production per vessel. To maintain an optimum sustainable yield during the present period of inflation, some operators have proposed subsidies, import taxes, import quotas, and limited entry. Speaking for myself, and I believe for a majority of the leadership in the shrimp industry, I do not favor subsidies because generally they serve only to help the marginal operator stay in business to further deplete the resource and compete with the more able fisherman. Import taxes and quotas on shrimp imports have also been proposed and federal legislation is pending. Since the United States depends heavily on imports to supply its domestic demand for shrimp, it is doubtful that Congress will enact such legislation in the near future.

Economists and biologists have shown that in order to maintain an optimum sustainable yield or an economically sound commercial fishery it is not only necessary to limit the total annual catch, but the number of fishermen as well. While this concept is certainly applicable to coastal species renewable each year such as shrimp, it is more important to the anadromous species and the far-ranging oceanic species whose life cycles cover several years, much of them in international waters. Some progress has been made in controlling the total catch through the various international conventions now in existence between the nations fishing the widely-ranging oceanic species. Such conventions, of course, are vital in any effort to maintain optimum sustainable yield of these species to both commercial and sports fishermen.

Limited entry as a management technique to help produce optimum sustainable yields of several important commercial species of fish is biologically and economically sound. If more than a certain number of fishermen fish for a given species at one time not only is the resource likely to be overfished, but the catch per fisherman will be so reduced that the entire fishery becomes economically marginal and nobody makes any money. The sociological and legal problems involved in any limited entry effort, however, are enormously complicated. For example, who will tell that boy from the bayou country of Louisiana who is today heading shrimp on the deck of his dad's boat that the great American dream is dead and that he can never have a chance to own a boat like his father's because there are no more shrimp fishing permits?

I have been involved in several limited entry programs. The discovery of high populations of brown shrimp off the coast of Texas in the late 1940's precipitated a fish rush not unlike the Alaskan gold rush. Shrimpers from all the Gulf states, principally from Florida, joined the Texas fleet in pursuit of the resource. Texas fishermen, by acts of the State legislature, attempted to prevent the entry of these out-of-state fishermen into the fishery. After a long and costly court battle the laws under which the out-of-state fishermen were denied licenses to fish within 9 miles of the coast, an area in the Gulf of Mexico claimed by Texas, or to land their catch in Texas ports, were declared discriminatory and therefore unconstitutional.

A second experiment with limited entry as a management tool involved the harvest of an under-utilized population of black drum (*Pogonias cromis*) in the lower Laguna Madre on the Texas coast. Under the provisions of the Rough Fish Removal Act a limited number of permits to harvest this annual crop were issued. Gill nets, otherwise illegal in this area, were authorized under the program. From a biologist's point of view the plan was ideal and accomplished a number of objectives. The annual commercial harvest of 5 million pounds of black drum not only provided substantial income to the licensed fishermen, but also reduced the competition between this species and red drum (*Sciaenops ocellata*), the angler's favorite species in this area. The removal of this surplus population of black drum also reduced the damage to bottom vegetation on which the major North American population of red head ducks (*Nyroca americana*) depends. The sociological and legal problems again entered the picture. The recreational fisherman was convinced that the commercial fishermen were taking thousands of pounds of protected species and everytime he saw a net in the bay he took his case to the press and to his representative in the state legislature. Finally, fishermen who had been denied these special licenses demanded equal privileges and took their case to the courts. Again, the law under which the program functioned was declared discriminatory and unconstitutional. The result has been the loss of possibly 50 million pounds of a valuable resource over the past 10 years, as well as the loss of other benefits.

Our knowledge of how to manage wildlife resources has often exceeded our knowledge of how to manage human resources. Our limitations in this area have been costly. We have often failed to convince the various resource user groups, the politicians, and even the administrators that our programs, both research and management, were sound, practical, and of ultimate benefit to the users. Much progress, however, has been made in recent years in this area. Frequent conferences between representatives of the National Marine Fisheries Service, the Sea Grant Program, and commercial and recreational fishermen are being held with good results. And, undoubtedly, the new marine extension program will help bridge the gap between commercial fishermen and the several government agencies involved in resource management.

As the world's demand for protein has increased so have the world's fishing fleets, and in many areas, particularly the North Pacific and the Continental Shelf of the North Atlantic, a number of important species have been so drastically reduced by overfishing that they no longer sustain an economically sound fishery. The development of highly efficient distant-water fishing fleets by the U.S.S.R.,

East Germany, Poland, Japan, and other countries has resulted in an invasion by these fleets into the traditional American fishing grounds. Cuban fishing fleets under Russian and Japanese tutelage are appearing off the Texas, Louisiana, and Mexican coasts in increasing numbers. Foreign fishing has not yet reached the level of competition with coastal fishermen in this area that it has off the New England coast or in the North Pacific. This will probably change too, making the management of marine resources in the Gulf of Mexico even more difficult than it is today.

Certain of these well equipped foreign fishing fleets now operating off our shores have no interest in optimum sustainable yield or even maximum sustainable yield but conduct their operations on a maximum yield basis, moving on to a new unexploited area once the resource is depleted and fishing becomes unprofitable. Many of the foreign flag fishing vessels operating over the Continental Shelf of the United States are subsidized or controlled by their governments. Thus American fishermen, operating entirely under a system of free enterprise, are not only in direct competition with foreign fishing fleets, but with some of the great maritime powers of the world whose resources in manpower and technology are enormous.

Controlling the harvest of oceanic species in international waters was a major consideration by the fishing nations of the world at the Law of the Sea Conference concluded in August of this year in Caracas, Venezuela. The American fisheries position at the Law of the Sea Conference was fragmented. All the diverse segments of American fisheries, both recreational and commercial, want the same thing—optimum sustainable yield of the species in which they have special interests. They differ, however, on how this can be accomplished. Those fishermen in New England and the Northwest Pacific who fish the coastal species believe that a 200-mile fishery zone would aid in helping them maintain these species at an optimum sustainable yield. The salmon interests, the tuna fishermen, and the distant water shrimp fishermen have different views and are convinced that such a move to 200 miles by the United States would act in a reverse manner for their interests and that all of the American fishermen can best be served by international agreements. Little was accomplished in this connection during the 1974 Law of the Sea Conference in Caracas and these matters will probably be the subject of international debates for years to come.

Research to provide the techniques necessary to manage the fishery resources of this country and, in fact, the world on an optimum sustainable yield basis has lagged far behind the world's demand for these resources. If we are to ultimately manage them on an optimum sustainable yield basis, and I think this is what we all want, although some of us may march to the sound of a different drummer, then all levels of government and the private sector as well in this country and abroad are going to have to provide a much higher level of research funding than they have in the past. The American Fisheries Society will again be called upon to provide the leadership as it has in the past. The road ahead will be rough and filled with disappointments. I am, however, convinced that your accomplishments in the future will be even greater than those in the past.

The Texas Shrimp Association, P.O. Box 1666, 305 First National Bank Building, Brownsville, Texas 78520

Optimum Sustainable Yield as a Management Concept in Recreational Fisheries

Frank E. Carlton

There is an old saying that conflict tends to clarify reality. The truth of that statement appears to become more evident with the passage of time, but this increased recognition only further emphasizes a more essential point that clarification of reality is not necessarily related to inevitable progress. It is also increasingly evident that although a vast array of social problems have a common basis, various scientific disciplines have not been able to achieve adequate solutions within the isolated area of their interests, or more importantly, unify a comprehensive approach to the fundamental difficulties they share. Therefore, recreational fisheries problems must be viewed as a relatively small manifestation of basic societal difficulties which are also expressed in other ways; and analysis of optimum sustainable yield (OSY) as a management concept must encompass fisheries considerations as well as the more comprehensive context of the value of recreation and natural resource utilization to society as a whole.

Recreational fishing is the ritual pursuit of pleasure associated with the experience. Its total value includes an aggregate of quantitative and qualitative factors which can be sufficiently defined to provide a rational basis for management. Quantitative factors include capital expenditures and opportunity costs which can be estimated by any of several different systems in order to provide a basis for comparison with alternative uses of the resource. Qualitative factors include the recreational value of escape from the pressures of of modern living as well as the primal satisfactions associated with the procurement of food. These qualitative factors can also be translated into economic units; again with sufficient validity for comparison with alter-

natives. The fact that these comparisons can be made requires three further considerations:

First, with regard to the relevance of establishing the economic worth of the recreational fisheries industry.

Those same factors that have forced the individual fisherman to perceive his collective jeopardy have also forced federal and state governments to recognize his identity as a political constituency. In the development of recreational fisheries management programs, assessment of industry worth is a justifiable exercise but it should not be confused with the importance of political support, or opposition, from a united and active constituency.

Second, the usefulness of comparing the economic worth of commercial versus recreational fisheries for the purpose of resource allocation.

The traditional conflicts between recreational and commercial fishermen have largely given way to the mutual dangers imposed by inadequate government supervision and uncontrolled fishing. Recreational and commercial fisheries are not so much concerned with preferential treatment based on greater economic utilization of common resources as they are with conservation of the resource itself. Fishermen from both pursuits realize that allocations made on the basis of economic comparisons alone cannot adequately deal with displacement of employment and redistribution of income and wealth. And further, these same fishermen see the politics associated with "Big Government" and international negotiations as a greater, more immediate threat than multi-user competition.

Third, further considerations concerning the quality of the recreational experience and its value.

The quality and value of the recreational

experience reflects the inadequacies of our daily occupations. Thoreau referred to this problem over one hundred years ago when he remarked that "The mass of men lead lives of quiet desperation." The tensions of business and personal life can be considered to have a reciprocal relationship to the quality of the recreational experience. Fishing is good because of the negative and injurious aspects of what we are getting away from and that degree of relief is directly expressed as the quality of pleasure derived from the recreational experience.

Fishing involves the additional advantage of recalling those primitive days when the primary pursuit of man was the procurement of food. The basic satisfaction of the hunt is fundamentally related to our identity and hence our happiness. The importance of the recreational experience to the individual is beyond question. Its value to society can be economically assessed by that amount society is willing to pay. As long as all users are mutually accommodated the cost of individual or industry access can serve as a conservation measure; but when all users cannot be accommodated, allocations must be made on the basis of society's prerogatives rather than those traditionally enjoyed by any individual. Allocation requires a two-phase cooperation between science and management which can not achieve success without recognition—and accommodation—of those social and political factors which actually influence decision and application. Examination of OSY from the recreational view must consider the development and applicability of models and concepts as well as relevant social and political considerations which have added to or detracted from the factual realization of management goals.

The purpose of this conference (analysis of fisheries utilization with regard to OSY as a management concept) would seem to imply criticism of previous fisheries models and suggest that development of better models is causally related to better fisheries management. This suggestion contains an inherent confusion regarding the function of science and the function of management. Over-ex-

ploitation of finite resources and the results of that misuse cannot be primarily attributed to the lack of data or to inadequate management concepts. This generalization is true with regard to fishery utilization as well as to the use of other natural resources. Management decisions are manifest in both the character of events and their temporal sequence. Management provides direction through the *timely* juxtaposition of available data to its relevant context. Therefore, the degree of success achieved is a function of the immediacy and effectiveness of the imposed change. Management is decision between alternatives. It is not science or scientific data, but rather the use of such data as they relate to a series of choices between alternatives. Science can describe those alternatives and predict consequences. Science itself cannot control the fishery or the fact of day-to-day attitudes and practices. Adequate management must involve anticipatory decisions which predict and control coming events rather than reflecting an exposition of what has already occurred. Adequate science must establish both objectives and consequences of proposed programs. But, rather than face the responsibility for misapplication of management concepts and misuse of the resource, industry and science frequently connive to generate a symbiotic avoidance of reality through the further production of more models and more management concepts which do not reflect real objectives and real consequences. Present examples include Maximum Sustainable Yield (MSY), Maximum Economic Yield (MEY), Maximum Net Economic Revenue, and Optimum Sustainable Yield (OSY).

There is nothing wrong with these models or with their application to fisheries problems. The fact of depleted stocks and extinct species is the result of human behavior contrary to the thrust of the management concept, e.g., the result of fishing for maximization of immediate profit through the direct violation of the MSY imperative to restrict effort at a given level. The MSY concept was developed to better define overfishing in the hope that predicting the lowest level of cost/effort to produce the maximum sustained amount of fish would lead to rational fishery practices. That it has not is a matter of record, but it must be clearly recognized that this failure was not primarily caused by a lack of data or an inadequate management concept. If fault is to be attributed it must be laid to several "real world" factors—the short-sightedness of fishermen, government subsidy of the industry and its practices, and society at large which is ultimately responsible for its own condition. This disparity between abstract and "real world" factors defines the paradox of human behavior and explains the necessity of recreation.

Analysis of these "real world" factors in an effort to define "optimum" emphasizes the consideration of factors which were present all the time. Optimum is a political word in that no one can disagree with the idea in principle, but translating that agreement into enforceable regulations has thus far been impossible. Examination of OSY from the recreational fisheries view may provide information leading a consensus regarding its definition and application.

OSY stipulates two criteria, optimum and sustainable yield. Optimum refers to that which is "best or most favorable." OSY must refer to that which is most favorable to the broad public interest, to the long-term interests of society, including the comprehensive requirements of social, economic, biological, and political factors as well as their interactions and relative values. Optimum can have its only relevance in this total context; but that same reasoning also requires the further comparison of all alternative uses to the value of the resource itself. One cannot assume any specific recreational activity is necessary to future society, nor is it legitimate management to pursue that goal directly.

As a management concept, then, optimum must refer to a standard which is relevant to the real practice of fishing and it must accommodate all users. Conversely, a significant majority of users must be willing to be mutually regulated. Unless the whole resource is controlled no "optimum" is possible. Therefore, recreational fisheries optimum is related to and dependent on total resource management.

Sustainable yield refers to a constant amount of catch produced by a given effort. In commercial fishing MSY implicitly involves the idea of "full utilization" which holds that any amount of catch less than the maximum which can be sustained is "wasted." This patent nonsense is offered despite the reduction of stocks below the normal level and the obvious consequences of significant losses to other uses of the resource including, for example, food for other fish and natural recycling.

The yield in recreational fishing is the quality of pleasure. This quality is not directly related to catch in terms of size, numbers, or elusiveness of the fish, but it is certainly related to the expectation of catching something. In those instances where a stock approaches extinction from any cause the quality of the recreational experience must decline. Since the yield of a quality of pleasure from recreational fishing requires only the opportunity of an occasional good catch, it is reasonable to assume that a level of stock maintained to support commercial interests would adequately accommodate recreational demands. Therefore, recreational fisheries goals must include rational commercial fishery management in addition to environmental protection and reasonable allocation of the resource.

Assessment of applicability of OSY requires a distinction between inland and marine problems. Inland recreational fisheries problems are relatively simple compared to their marine counterparts, if for no other reason than the involvement of international politics in the latter. A more important distinction, however, is the fundamental difference in the attitude of the user with regard to proprietorship of the resource. Inland natural resources, including fisheries, are recognized as an established public trust, with custody and management exercised by the states on behalf of their citizens. In a real sense, everyone "owns" the resource and feels a sense of responsibility toward it. Marine natural resources beyond the twelve-mile fisheries zone, on the other hand, belong to no one. No one "owns" or has preferential rights to ocean fisheries stocks or to other associated resources. The former assumption leads to democratic cooperation and the latter to *laissez faire* exploitation. Until that twelve-mile limit is extended to include the geographic extent of our marine resources no management program is possible.

OSY has been compared with MEY in the sense that limitation of cost in order to maximize profit is similar in concept to optimum in the utilization of less resource than that required for full utilization (MSY). Comparing OSY to MEY does not define optimum and is misleading to the extent that it assumes the optimum level will always be less than the maximum sustainable, clearly an unwarranted assumption. OSY could conceivably be identical to or exceed MSY.

The individual fisherman must be disenchanted with a purely scientific approach to solving the very problems which have been largely caused by the lopsided application of science and technology to the utilization of fisheries resources. The simple fisherman sees the scientist as more concerned with abstractions than with the fact of depleted stocks and extinct species. In a similar sense the fisherman sees government functions contaminated by special interest politics which adulterate the democratic obligation to the broad public interest and specifically to the rational utilization of natural resources as a public trust.

The prime recreational fisheries management goal is not how to conserve the resource nor, conversely, how to exploit it for maximum economic return. It is the establishment of rational cooperation among present users, adequate mission-oriented research to determine the long-term values of the resource to society, and initiation of policy to evoke the changes necessary to insure the realization of those values. The recreational fisheries do not need a new concept as much as a new commitment to management *per se* to the development of real regulations and their actual enforcement. The exact mechanism of the program matters not nearly so much as its

effectiveness, as its translation into the material reality of fishermen and fish.

From these considerations of OSY as a management concept for recreational fisheries, three conclusions can be expressed:

First, fisheries models and concepts preceding OSY are rational in context and not causally related to the continuance of irrational fisheries practices. The success of this conference in achieving a definition of OSY and consensus with regard to its application can not provide assurance of an increased probability of improvement.

Second, OSY can be sufficiently defined as a management concept for recreational fisheries. A real solution to fisheries problems, however, rests not so much with this academic exercise as it does with the social and political aspects of a rational basis for day-to-day management. To date, this management has not been achieved because sufficient societal pressures did not exist to change traditional patterns of thought and behavior.

And third, recreational fisheries problems reflect that same fundamental difficulty seen in all natural resource utilization today, namely the wide disparity between material reality and abstract concept, between management principles and daily practice. The single fundamental assumption which contributes to the perpetuation of this disparity is the belief that demand must increase inexorably, and that supply must keep pace with that increase, in order to maintain the standard of living.

The basic question has now become whether growth itself is an optimum condition for the continuance of society.

Philosophers have pondered this question for thousands of years. The fact that the average man is now becoming aware of this problem and wants a solution is a reassuring indication that the required changes will become a reality for us all.

Literature Cited

BRYAN, R. C. 1974. The dimensions of a salt-water sport fishing trip, or What do people look for in a fishing trip besides fish? Environment Canada. Fish. and Mar. Serv. PAC/T-74-1. 35 pp.

CASSIDY, P. A. 1973. Commonality, fishery resources, potential and policy: Comment. Amer. J. Agric. Econ. Aug. 1973: 526–529.

CICCHETTI, C. J. and V. K. SMITH. 1972. Recreation benefit estimation and forecasting: Implications of the identification problem. Water Resources Res. 8(4): 840–850.

FISCHER, DAVID W. 1973. Some social and economic aspects of marine resource development. Amer. J. Econ. and Soc. 32(2): 113–127.

FULLENBAUM, F., E. CARLSON, and F. W. BELL. 1972. On models of commercial fishing: A defense of the traditional literature. J. Polit. Econ. July–August 1972: 761–768.

HOLMAN, MARY A. and J. T. BENNETT. 1973. Determinants of use of water-based recreational facilities. Water Resources Res. 9(5): 1209–1218.

McFADDEN, J. T. 1969. Trends in freshwater sport fisheries of North America. Trans. Amer. Fish. Soc. 98(1): 136–150.

O'ROURKE, A. 1973. Commonality, fishery resources, potential and policy: Reply. Am. J. Agric. Econ. Aug. 1973: 530–531.

SOILEAU, L. D., K. C. SMITH, R. HUNTER, C. E. KNIGHT, D. K. TABBERER, and D. W. HAYNE. 1972. Atchafalaya Basin usage study interim report. A cooperative study, Louisiana Wild Life and Fisheries Commission and U.S. Army Corps of Engineers, New Orleans District. July 1, 1971–June 30, 1972. 28 pp.

SPORT FISHING INSTITUTE. 1974. SFI Directors' resolutions. SFI Bull. 255: 1–3.

STEVENS, J. B. 1969. Measurement of economic values in sport fishing: An economist's views on validity, usefullness, and propriety. Trans. Amer. Fish. Soc. 98(2): 352–357.

STROUD, RICHARD H. 1974. Fisheries management in the coastal zone. SFI Bull. 254: 1–3.

National Coalition for Marine Conservation, Inc., P.O. Box 3458, Savannah, Georgia 31403

Multidisciplinary Aspects of Optimum Sustainable Yield

John P. Harville

This symposium has been convened to evaluate the concept of optimum sustainable yield as a guiding principle for fisheries management. Clearly such a discussion should be developed within real-world terms of reference which consider both the kinds of fisheries to be managed and the socioeconomic goals of the management decision-makers. Optimum sustainable yield (OSY) and maximum sustainable yield (MSY) are indistinguishable to operators of factory ships and catcher-boats engaged in single-purpose harvest of distant-water stocks—and both concepts are of course irrelevant where pulse-fishing strategies ignore long-term conservation goals.

The optimum sustainable yield concept has particular utility for management of fisheries which are subject to multiple uses and misuses, a condition descriptive of most of the fisheries in the developed countries. Whenever substantial components of a society perceive diversified values for a given stock of fish, parallel divergence of management goals will follow. Challenges can be expected against management criteria designed to support only a single-use category, since those criteria usually do not adequately satisfy the needs of alternative uses having different values.

Too often these challenges to single-purpose management criteria generate only indirect responses, and in the political rather than the scientific arena. Fisheries scientists are inclined to avoid multiple-use problems, usually through the simple expedient of defining the scope of their own functions in terms of pursuit of MSY. By identifying their own goals with those of a particular supporting constituency, fisheries scientists can retreat in reasonable comfort to concentrate totally on maximizing the pounds or numbers made

available for harvest by that constituency—consistent, of course, with long-term preservation of the stocks. Those goals are uncomplicated and straightforward, and are served by objectively gathered numerical data interpreted according to respected formulas and models. This self-imposed delimitation of scope enables the scientist to take the view that other user demands on the same resource are "not in his shop."

Where other users of the same resource perceive different values and compete for a different kind of yield, a parallel scientific group may be operating according to a similar working plan but toward a quite different end product. This dichotomous approach to management leads inexorably to competitive chaos. Furthermore, if the fisheries scientist persists in defining himself out of researches based on multiple-use demands, management decision-making can become essentially a contest of power in the political arena, with participants deprived of the factual background information required for rational judgments.

Clearly the convenors of this symposium and its participants view the concept of optimum sustainable yield as a mechanism to avoid this fragmented approach to management decision-making. While fisheries scientists may be more comfortable with the objective components of MSY, they do recognize the technical and philosophical difficulties inherent in that concept as reviewed earlier by Royce and Radovich. The next needed step is to establish an operational imperative for optimum use evaluations by fisheries scientists and managers, despite the intellectually disturbing problems inherent in subjective determination of what is optimal and for whom.

For analytical purposes, alternative uses

and values for fisheries may be arrayed into categories as in the following sections. In actual practice, of course, management policy decisions usually are made fishery by fishery, and in each instance, management decision-makers are subjected, overtly or covertly, to a permutation of pressures reflecting the relative strengths and perceived importance of alternative uses and values.

Multidisciplinary approaches are required for effective evaluation of multiple use problems. Political scientist Brewster Denny has effectively illustrated the inherently interdisciplinary nature of public policy decisions in resources management, using salmon fisheries as an example (in Crutchfield 1965). He noted that the central public policy issue of regulating a salmon fishery through limiting the catch "begins with the biologist's discussion of the habits of the salmon, continues with the lawyer's discussion of the legal nature of the resource and its management, includes the economist's concern for efficient use of gear, and the politician's concern for proper allocation of water among fishermen and other users."

The implications for fisheries science are obvious. If fisheries scientists would constructively influence decisions of an interdisciplinary nature, they must broaden the scope of professional output to encompass economic, legal, sociologic, and general environmental perspectives. However, broadened scientific advice is not the only factor influencing a society's resource management decisions. As Denny phrases it: "Answers and solutions to the major resource problems can emerge only from the tough bargaining of the political process and relentless forces from the market place. But perspective and sensitivity as well as scientific knowledge can make this process both more representative and more responsible."

This process of political decision-making is particularly difficult in a developed country such as the United States, where multiple demands on limited fisheries resources produce often highly competitive political pressures. The free enterprise economy, operating through the democratic process, powerfully influences the decision-making process. Denny called particular attention to the sociopolitical root to this implementation problem in his assertion that "the critical public policy question for democratic societies in the second half of the twentieth century [is]: Can we effectively plan for and make wise use of our limited resources through the democratic political process and the free-market economy?"

This general sociopolitical question can be rephrased in the context of the present symposium to address particularly the applicability of the optimum sustainable yield concept to real-world fisheries problems, and to consider also the necessary institutional capabilities to convert that concept to management practice. First then, are we as fisheries scientists prepared to acknowledge the multiple-use requirements of most fisheries, and as a consequence, to expand the scope of our professional inquiry well beyond the familiar and relatively comfortable biological parameters of MSY considerations alone? Second, and certainly of a higher order of difficulty, can our free enterprise democratic society develop both the political will and the institutional mechanisms to transmute OSY scientific output into productive management action?

Alternative Uses and Values as Factors Influencing Fisheries Management

Maximum Sustainable Harvest for Food and Industrial Purposes

The harvest of selected fish species for food and industrial purposes dominates man's present uses of the world's fisheries resources. For most major ocean fisheries, alternative demands are essentially nonexistent or noncompetitive in impact; thus optimum sustainable yield is conceptually equivalent to maximum sustainable yield. This synonymy is implicit in Article 2 of the 1958 Fishing Convention of the UN Conference on Law of the Sea:

As employed in this Convention, the expression 'conservation of the living resources of the high seas' means the aggregate of the measures rendering possible the optimum sustainable yield from those resources so as to secure a maximum supply of food and other marine products.

Maximum sustainable yield (called optimum in the 1958 Convention) in the context of maximum physical production continues to be a cornerstone of the United States position on Law of the Sea. A corollary of this position is the principle of full utilization, which states that where any stock of fish is not being fully harvested by local fishermen, the fishermen of other nations should be guaranteed access to harvest the surplus. In August, 1971, Ambassador John R. Stevenson, head of the U.S. delegation to the preparatory conference for Law of the Sea deliberation, restated both the basis and the substance of this full utilization principle as follows (Stevenson 1971):

In previous statements we have emphasized the need to avoid a result which would in practice reduce the supply of protein from the sea. We should bear in mind that although fish constitute a relatively small part of the total protein eaten by man, it is one of the important contributors to animal protein which is vital to human nutrition. In many developing countries [and] . . . to many millions of people, fish protein is by far the major source of animal protein available. It is thus essential to the nutrition of a substantial part of the world population.

Accordingly, we do not consider it wise to give any State the right to prevent or encumber fishing for portions of stocks that State cannot harvest itself for the time being, except, of course, in the case of appropriate conservation matters.

Ambassador Stevenson's caveat with respect to the full utilization principle; "except, of course, in the case of appropriate conservation matters" has potentially significant implications in the context of draft articles submitted to the Conference by the U.S. Delegation a few days before United Nations General Assembly (1971). These stated in part:

Conservation measures shall be adopted that do not discriminate in form or in fact against any fisherman. For this purpose, the allowable catch shall be . . . designed to maintain the maximum sustainable yield or restore it as soon as practicable, taking into account relevant environmental and economic factors.

Some observers interpret this reference to "relevant environmental and economic factors" as opening the way to incorporation of economic and social criteria into sustained yield calculations, and therefore into determination of full utilization of the resource. However, Ambassador Stevenson's July 1974 plenary session speech at the Caracas Law of the Sea Conference again reiterated basic U.S.

support of MSY and full utilization of fisheries resources.

In a world generally short of food and particularly hungry for protein, food from the sea quite rightly holds very high priority in international planning for uses of the sea. However, it should be emphasized that a narrow interpretation of the full utilization principle constitutes total commitment to a single-use philosophy of fisheries management. When linked to the MSY concept, it forecloses options for future management of internationally vulnerable species according to any other goals and values. Under a system of international agreements based upon a full utilization, maximum physical yield requirement, a coastal nation could not elect to maintain coastal stocks at levels above those dictated by MSY in order to realize certain socioeconomic or ecological values (e.g., to increase economic yield, or provide forage for other more valued species, or maintain local concentrations of fish for particular benefits). Under the principle of full utilization for food and related purposes *sensu stricto*, population levels above those specified for MSY would be considered surpluses available for harvest by fishermen of other nations.

It is a key premise of this paper that the full utilization principle must be considered in the broader context of the 1971 exceptions set forth in the U.S. position, "taking into account relevant environmental and economic factors," so as not to unnecessarily foreclose a coastal nation's prerogative to assign multiple-use values to a given fishery resource and to manage it accordingly. The sections that follow indicate something of the range of these alternative uses and their attendant values.

It should be noted that current national resurgences in planning for the future of U.S. fisheries and for the rejuvenation of the U.S. commercial fishing industry recognize and support alternative fisheries uses and values even though primary emphasis is accorded fisheries for food and related industrial purposes. Three examples, two originating from the Congress and one from the Executive branch of government, indicate these multiple use concerns.

The Eastland Resolution, passed unanimously by both Houses of Congress in 1974, recognizes the decline of position of the United States as a major fishing nation, the growing obsolescence of commercial fishing fleets, the decreases in their production of food fish and fish products, and the damaging impact of foreign competition. It affirms the policy of the Congress that the U.S. fishing industry be accorded all support required to strengthen it, and that all necessary steps be taken to protect coastal fisheries against excessive foreign fishing. Senator James O. Eastland's speech introducing this Resolution on the floor of the Senate (Congressional Record, February 7, 1973) emphasized his central concern for the serious plight of U.S. commercial fisheries and seafood processors, but also stressed the need to include sport fishing interests and the requirements of other user groups in development of a national policy for fisheries management.

In December 1973, Senator Warren Magnuson and 55 cosponsors introduced a resolution to authorize a National Ocean Policy study by a special Committee comprised of the leaders of other concerned Senate Committees (Congressional Record, December 19, 1973). As subsequently approved by the Senate, this resolution recognizes the importance of depletable ocean resources as future sources of protein, new materials, and energy; the need to resolve conflicts of national and international jurisdiction over the ocean; the need to protect the quality of the marine environment; and the importance of a clear and comprehensive ocean policy. Among its objectives, the resolution calls for:

. . . establishing policies to achieve the goal of full utilization and conservation of living resources of the oceans and recommending solutions to problems in marine fisheries and their management, rehabilitation of United States fisheries, as well as aquaculture and the extraction of drugs from the sea.

The resolution elsewhere indicates that values other than full utilization and conservation must be considered, and calls for implementation of coastal zone management by assessing problems, needs, and jurisdictional capabilities with respect to "information sources, recreation needs, pollution problems, population trends, and future pressures on the coastal zone." Since the coastal zone includes the waters subtending the shoreline, these problems and needs clearly relate to a wide array of alternative uses of marine resources.

As a third example of a current national planning effort, in late 1973 the National Marine Fisheries Service began development of a long-range National Fisheries Plan designed to integrate and serve the diverse needs and goals of all fisheries user groups. This effort was in direct response to a call for urgent action by the National Advisory Committee on Oceans and Atmosphere (NACOA). In 1972 that call set only a single national goal: to increase substantially (from 40% to 50%) the share of fish supplied to the domestic market by domestic fishermen (National Advisory Committee on Oceans and Atmosphere 1973).

In 1973 the NACOA Report identified six conditions necessary to bring about an "atmosphere for redevelopment" of national fisheries which would reestablish confidence in continued availability of the resource and would create an attractive economic climate for encouragement of private enterprise. These conditions recognized that fisheries, as a part of our national wealth, must be husbanded; that this means conservation by agreement, regulation, and uniform national and international enforcement; and that jurisdictional problems, while difficult, are capable of solution through negotiation. Most important for the interdisciplinary aspects of the present symposium, a fourth condition states (op. cit. pp. 42–43):

Conservation is not realistically achievable by biological management considerations alone. The Federal government also must work out an approach to economic regulation of the industry with due regard for historic rights and social consequences. NACOA believes that unless there is a limit to fishing effort, the inherent surge to overcapitalization in any successful fishery will soon make it marginal . . .

While the National Fisheries Plan presently under development emphasizes production and harvest of fish for food and industrial purposes, its statement of mission appears very much like an alternative expression of the optimum sustainable yield concept:

Optimize the economic, social and aesthetic value of fisheries to the Nation consistent with maintaining fisheries resources for the future.

The draft plan outline (in press) identified four goals for implementation of that mission:

Restore and maintain fisheries stocks of interest to the U.S.
Develop and maintain healthy commercial and recreational fishing industries.
Improve the contribution of marine resources to recreation and other social benefits.
Increase the supply of wholesome, competitively priced fishery products to the consumer.

Implementation of Senator Eastland's Congressional Resolution and review and refinement of the Administration's National Fisheries Plan both will involve broadly based regional and local assessment and input. Therefore they should reflect reasonable representation of multiple-use interests. These plans and policies can be expected to develop central thrusts toward improvement of the position of commercial fisheries in the nation and the world, and toward full utilization of selected stocks for food and industrial purposes. However, the calls to action which generated these efforts also specify concern for recreational, economic, and environmental aspects of fisheries conservation and development. Certainly these interdisciplinary problems call for multidisciplinary responses in the context of optimizing the yield from the fisheries concerned.

In summary, the examples cited have stressed a growing awareness at higher political levels that while fisheries management must emphasize harvest of fish for food and industrial purposes, it cannot properly ignore other uses and values. It also should be recognized that for many fisheries, maximum sustainable harvest for food and industrial purposes very well may be an entirely appropriate single purpose, since no significant competitive use is immediately foreseeable. The caution must be advanced, however, that our knowledge of ecological relationships is too fragmentary to assure us beyond reasonable doubt that massive harvests of any given species will not materially affect another spe-

cies of greater value to us. Recent controversies over hake harvests are a case in point. Where hake was once disregarded as a species not desired by U.S. fishermen and thus fully available for foreign harvest, concerns have been expressed recently that its overharvest may have a negative impact on locally desirable species for which it is a source of forage.

A simple MSY approach to fisheries management appears easiest to defend for a fishery which is limited physically and therefore ecologically relatively well understood, and for which maximum sustainable harvest is the only perceived value. These conditions do not apply to most ocean fisheries. Certain commercial and recreational fisheries in freshwater impoundments approximate these criteria, particularly where the environment has been sufficiently degraded that the quality of the fishing experience has little significance to the recreational fisherman.

Harvests for Optimum Value at Immature Stages

In some fisheries, local custom and demand induce a harvest at immature stages, a procedure contrary to maximum physical yield goals, yet strongly supported by local economic or sociologic influences. Three quite unlike instances illustrate this application of optimum yield criteria to practical management situations.

Over wide areas of Southeast Asia, flourishing artisanal fisheries harvest larval gobies for preparation of a highly nutritious salted and fermented fish paste called *bagoong*. After three to five weeks of ripening in 5-gallon cans or earthen jugs, this product is considered ready for the table (though as in the curing of wine, the quality of the product is said to improve with age). In many areas of Southeast Asia, *bagoong* provides much of the necessary animal protein for the majority of the working class, served as a condiment with rice or corn (Manacop 1953).

Since harvest in many locations is by woven weirs which may totally barricade a stream, conservation measures are long overdue. However, in addition to providing nutritional benefits for people who need them greatly, this fishery and its products are deeply rooted in the customs and folkways of the culture. These nutritional and social benefit factors do not fit MSY equations, but become highly significant elements in optimum yield planning of management practices.

The goby fry *bagoong* fishery offers no conflicts with alternative harvest options, since adult gobies are confined to boulder-strewn rocky beds of river headwaters and are seldom subject to significant harvest. In contrast, the following two examples concern fisheries subject to intense user-group conflicts for harvest of a limited resource. In both instances one element of the fishery intentionally harvests smaller size classes in order to enjoy certain economic or social benefits. In both instances other fishermen harvest the same species for food or industrial purposes in accordance with MSY full utilization principles. Since maximum physical yield usually subsumes fullest possible growth prior to harvest, the taking of immature fish having significant remaining growth potential is vigorously opposed by these harvesters.

As first example, many recreational fisheries require bait of a particular size, and in some cases these preferred baits are the smaller size-classes of important commercial species. Southern California sport fishermen's demand for northern anchovies (*Engraulis mordax*) in the smaller age classes for live-bait purposes has created a flourishing bait-fish fishery which annually harvests in excess of 5,000 tons (Messersmith 1969).

Fisheries biologists estimate the total annual biomass of northern anchovies in the California Current system at 4 to 5 million tons. A commercial reduction fishery, operating under stringent quota limitations, exerts continuing pressure on California's Fish and Game Commission to be permitted to augment significantly its harvest of this very large biomass for fish food and fish product uses. These fishermen regard failure to permit this augmentation as unnecessary wastage of a valuable natural resource.

These differences in perceived values generate strong economic, social, and political pressures upon management decisions and decision-makers. Sportsmen covet the anchovy as the most desirable live bait available, and therefore vigorously oppose as a threat to that bait supply any significant commercial reduction fishery. This opposition is bolstered by memories of runaway growth of the sardine (*Sardinops sagax*) reduction fishery in the thirties and early forties, and the subsequent crash decline of the sardine population. To illustrate the strength of this opposition, a recent California Department of Fish and Game news release indicates that in August 1974 the Fish and Game Commission received petitions containing 66,000 signatures calling for a three-year moratorium on the taking of anchovies for reduction within the 12-mile limit.

The second example relates to coho and chinook salmon (*Oncorhynchus kisutch, O. tshawytscha*) fisheries of the Pacific Northwest. The rapid ocean growth of these valuable species argues strongly for permitting them to achieve full growth prior to harvest in order to maximize the physical yield from the resource. This premise underpins continuing U.S. efforts to reduce the devastating impact upon the resource by Japanese high seas gill-netters, who each year take large numbers of immature salmon and thereby decimate the runs produced in U.S. lakes and rivers.

This full-growth objective precipitates major gear and user-group conflicts within U.S. fisheries, where ocean trollers and seiners, gill-netters in the rivers and estuaries, and other freshwater fishermen compete for the stocks which have survived the Japanese high seas gill nets. As in the case of harvest of smaller-size anchovies and herring, certain economic and social benefits can be claimed for ocean harvest of coho and chinook salmon still having significant growth potential. Commercial ocean trollers cite premium prices paid for ocean-caught fish taken in bright prime condition (as contrasted with the more variable quality of fully mature fish harvested in the rivers). Sports fishermen emphasize, and pay handsomely for, the intangible but highly rated recreational values of the ocean angling experience. In both instances, these economic and social benefit arguments are contested by river and estuary fishermen willing to accept only maximum physical yield as a valid goal, and therefore bitterly opposed to the ocean troll harvest as wasteful of the resource. As with the anchovies, these differing concepts of values fan the fires of conflict for a limited and highly valuable fisheries resource.

With respect to management of Pacific salmon, fisheries scientists recently developed and sought public acceptance for a set of management objectives which recognize the multiple demands placed upon the salmon resource and the differing values which condition those demands. In 1972 the salmon scientists of the five Pacific States jointly advocated Pacific Marine Fisheries Commission approval of a resolution setting forth those objectives. The resolution failed to win approval due to vigorous opposition by commercial fishing interests to the portion of the statement which recognized different objectives for recreational and commercial harvests of salmon. In 1973, after further highly partisan debate, a slightly reworded resolution was approved by 3-2 vote of the participating States (Pacific Marine Fisheries Commission 1974).

The resolution emphasizes that the objectives articulate a composite goal for salmon management, all components of which must be considered in the evaluation of any comprehensive management plan. Maintenance of optimum escapement for spawning is one such objective. Three others are particularly illustrative of the optimum sustainable yield concept:

Recognize that the yield of the salmon fishery includes food value, dollar value, recreational value, and certain sociological values, and that all of these values must be considered in the regulation and management of the fisheries;

Maximize the sustained yield of chinook and coho salmon with due consideration of all of the values listed above;

Maximize the poundage yield to the commercial fishery by minimizing the taking in that fishery of chinook and coho salmon having significant remaining growth potential; however, recognize that the desired yield to the sport fishery is primarily in the recreational value of the fish caught, not in pounds produced, and therefore that optimum value does not necessarily require harvesting only mature fish.

Management to Protect and Improve the Ecosystem

Fisheries scientists and the informed public are evidencing increasing concern for the indirect impact of fisheries harvests on other components of the ecosystem. For example, the determined opposition in southern California to any expansion of the commercial anchovy fishery gathers much of its strength from the knowledge that anchovies are major components in the diets of highly prized food and game fishes. California Department of Fish and Game studies in 1968–69 showed that in southern California waters, anchovies comprised 56% of the diet for albacore (*Thunnus alalunga*), 76% for Pacific bonito (*Sarda chiliensis*), and 80% for bluefin tuna (*T. thynnus*) (Pinkas, Oliphant, and Iverson 1971). Fishermen harvesting those valuable species want no tampering with the forage which supports these multi-million dollar fisheries. In the Pacific northwest, similar public concerns are being expressed that the huge Soviet fishery for Pacific hake (*Merluccius productus*) in the eastern North Pacific may be reducing the forage provided by juvenile hake for salmon and other valuable food and game species.

Probably in part because of a growing public awareness that ocean resources have finite limits, persons other than ecologists are interested in the potential effects on the ecosystem of proposed new fisheries for underutilized species. Particularly where those target species are near the base of the oceanic food web, there is need to know whether major harvests are likely to interfere significantly with the food requirements of other desired species.

The pelagic red crab, *Pleuroncodes planipes*, illustrates this problem. It is presently unharvested on a commercial scale, yet is widely available in harvestable concentrations in the eastern tropical Pacific. Given improved fishing and processing technology, the pelagic red crab could become an important new fishery.

However, in the Baja California region, red crabs also constitute a principal forage species for both yellowfin and skipjack tunas (*Thun-*

nus albacares; *Euthynnus pelamis*). During periods of active upwelling, red crabs are most abundant in the cool upwelling water which provides their phytoplankton food. During those periods, tunas tend to aggregate in the warmer waters around the edges of the cool upwelling areas in order to feed on the locally abundant red crabs (Blackburn 1969). The possibility must be considered that a major fishery for red crabs could significantly reduce the food supply available to tunas, and also disrupt the aggregation mechanisms which influence their availability to fishermen.

Ecological considerations can generate quite a different kind of fisheries management planning, designed to increase the harvest of one species in order to provide ecological room for the population growth of a competing species. In 1964 the California Cooperative Oceanic Fisheries Investigations (CalCOFI) proposed an ecological experiment to assist the return of the sardine as a viable fishery. In a paper based on 1951–59 data, the scientists noted that spectacular increases in anchovy populations closely followed the rapid decline of the sardine population induced by heavy fishing in the 1930's and 1940's. They suggested that "there is a real chance that simultaneously reducing the pressure on sardines and imposing pressure on anchovies will reverse the present equilibrium and assist in bringing back the more valuable sardine. This constitutes an exciting opportunity for marine science to assist society in meeting its complex needs." (Messersmith, Baxter, and Roedel 1969).

Primarily because of strong and well organized opposition by recreational fishermen and the party-boat operators to any increase in the reduction harvest of anchovies, this proposal was not approved and the experiment never undertaken. In the context of multi-use competition for a single stock and accordant need for multidisciplinary approaches to fisheries research and management, four special-interest groups exerted varying influences on that decision-making process: the *fisheries biologists*, who recommended experimental increases in the anchovy harvest to test their hypothesis for bringing back the sardines and increasing the commercial yield; the *commercial fishing industry*, which pressed for increased quotas for the anchovy reduction fishery; the *bait fishing industry* and *sport fishermen*, who unyieldingly opposed any increase in the anchovy harvest; and the *decision-makers* themselves, who were concerned over allocation of the resource and other political problems not necessarily related to the anchovy fishery.

Economic Aspects of Fisheries Management

Earlier in this symposium, Dr. James Crutchfield most effectively reviewed this key element of the interdisciplinary approach to fisheries management. All participants are aware of the growing recognition—even among biologists—that fisheries management involves people as well as fish. All are aware, too, that even where official mandates call for management actions restricted to conservation of the resource, economic considerations also will influence the decision-making process. Perhaps most important in terms of constructive action, fisheries scientists are accepting the premise that in a free enterprise society, fisheries management must be reasonably supportive of economic viability for the fishing industry. Among other things this requires finding a solution to the overcapitalization problems associated with exploitation of unowned resources.

The point was made above, and only half facetiously, that even biologists are beginning to accept the necessity for strong economic input to fisheries research and management. It should be emphasized that this must be a reciprocal process—that for a truly interdisciplinary information output there must be a multidisciplinary input. This requires that biologists and economists seek the common ground of needed mutual support, and develop the communication attitudes and mechanisms necessary for team action. In plain practical terms, this demands inclusion of economists on a full-time total commitment basis on the fisheries research and management team.

It is encouraging to note that in some

programs this operational integration already is under way. As one example, the State/ Federal Fisheries Management Program for Dungeness crab, *Cancer magister* (jointly supported by the National Marine Fisheries Service and the States of California, Oregon, and Washington) in 1973 organized a study team comprised of two economists and one fisheries biologist for a three-year study designed to produce a rational coastwide management plan. In the first year of that study, fusion of biological and economic approaches and techniques has been mandatory in order to develop the information base for decisions concerning regulation of fishery seasons. Crabs reach optimum harvest conditions at progressively later dates from south to north, and alternatives in opening fishing dates along the coast involve a complex interaction of potential biological and economic effects. This same study team will focus primary attention over the next two years on evaluating alternatives for reducing excess effort in the crab harvesting industry.

Fisheries Management to Enhance Aesthetic Values

Other participants in this symposium have stressed the fact that the recreational fisherman is primarily interested in a highly variable and nearly undefinable value—the *quality* of his fishing experience. Physical yield can contribute significantly to his perception of that quality, as in the case of the catchable trout fisherman waiting for the hatchery truck to off-load its cargo. At the opposite extreme, ultimate angling satisfaction may involve a physical yield of zero to the flycasting enthusiast on a catch-and-release quality fishing stream.

This recognition that angling success can not be quantified solely on the basis of physical yield has been honored by fisheries managers far more in theory than in practice. Perhaps this reflects in part the pervasive impact of MSY as fisheries dogma—also the neat convenience of being able to quantify program success in terms of pounds or numbers harvested by users. Clearly the task of defining and measuring the quality of an aesthetic experience requires techniques and approaches not normally addressed in the university curriculum for fisheries biologists. The need for a multidisciplinary attack upon this formidable task is self-evident, particularly since for political purposes some sort of cost-effectiveness assessment ultimately must be developed.

This need for quantification of the recreational experience is particularly cogent where recreational and commercial interests compete for a limited resource. Here it seems imperative that a single research team should undertake assessment of benefits to both groups, not because methods will be similar but because they must be reciprocally credible. Mutual acceptance of results is far less likely when separate studies are undertaken by separate groups. Each may be suspected of a measure of vested interest, and differences in philosophy and approach may further impede the communication process.

The following relatively simple example illustrates the practical need for quantification of benefits to recreational as well as commercial fishermen. In 1973, its five member States directed the Pacific Marine Fisheries Commission to undertake a comparative study of tax and license fees among the Pacific States toward the object of encouraging greater uniformity of these costs to the users. The States also requested an analysis of comparative expenditures in order to review the relationships of revenues generated to benefits received by the several user groups.

In the State of Oregon, for fiscal year 1973, $4,354,000 were expended for hatchery production of chinook and coho salmon by Oregon's two management agencies (Fish Commission of Oregon and Oregon Wildlife Commission). Since salmon must run the gauntlet of many potential harvesters in their total migration pathway, there is no rational way to determine *a priori* how many will be harvested by each user group. How then can benefits be estimated? Catch statistics indicate that in Oregon recreational fishermen harvested approximately 400,000 salmon in fiscal year 1973, and commercial fishermen caught 1,240,000. Does this indicate a three-to-one advantage in benefits to commercial fishermen? It does only if one assumes that a fish has equal worth caught in either fishery—clearly not the case if the quality of the experience rather than the pounds of flesh yielded is the true value to the recreational fisherman. But on what basis can the quality of the angling experience be estimated and assigned an approximate value? Might a multidisciplinary team give us both the figures and a defensible rationale for these estimates?

The aesthetic values of fisheries usually are considered essentially in terms of the quality of the angling experience. Fisheries management also must concern itself increasingly with public benefits from nonextractive use of fisheries resources. Here again, the quality of the aesthetic experience must be recognized and to the extent possible must be quantified. Growing numbers of strongly motivated people visit fish hatcheries and spawning channels, charter vessels to observe and photograph migrations of whales or concentrations of other sea-life, employ glass-bottomed boats or SCUBA gear to view the profusion of organisms at an underwater park, and engage in a myriad of other nonextractive uses of fisheries resources. Along rocky shores, vast numbers visit tidepools and surge channels. In the aggregate their impact may be so severe on these accessible natural microcosms that protective laws must be enacted to limit collection and disturbance (e.g., California's recent regulations prohibiting collection of tidepool organisms except under permit).

For educational reasons and a multiplicity of social benefits, these nonextractive uses should be encouraged through aggressive information and education programs. As these uses grow in popularity, they also must be regulated. Both processes require financing, and budgets for these purposes will depend in part on effective cost-benefit arguments. While in no sense can the values of aesthetic and educational experiences be expressed only in dollars, the effort must be made to progress as effectively as possible with that quantification process.

Fisheries management goals and the quality of life

Only relatively affluent and well-developed nations can afford the luxury of recreational fisheries for their own citizens. In most developing countries, fisheries resources must be reserved for food, or perhaps for sale on the foreign market to bolster foreign exchange. To the people of such countries, recreational fisheries actually may appear an affront—a wastage of resources needed elsewhere to feed hungry people. The fact that most sport-caught fish also are eaten may be overlooked, since sport fishing descriptions generally emphasize only "fishing for fun" aspects.

A symposium on optimum sustainable yield inevitably will be less meaningful in less well-developed and less affluent societies, since many of the values described as options for optimization will not there be perceived as values. However, maximum physical yield may not be the preferred target either. Instead, a nation may choose to use its fisheries resources to confer a particular social benefit upon its people. As in many other instances, optimum *yield* might better be called optimum *use*, since the goal may not be physical harvest so much as a desired quality of life.

At the recent (1973) FAO Technical Conference on Fishing Management and Development in Vancouver, British Columbia, delegates speaking for a number of nations outlined national fisheries goals primarily in terms of needed social benefits. An FAO official well summarized the need in developing countries for assistance to small-scale fisheries for improvements on their fishing, processing, and marketing, and therefore in their standard of living: "In many countries and for many groups of small-scale fishermen, social objectives related to employment and producer living standards are likely to be of greater importance than economic objectives related to their contribution to the market economy" (Proude 1973).

India's delegate underscored the same concept and added another, citing two objectives for rationalizing India's labor-intensive small-scale fisheries. "On the one hand, they provide direct and indirect employment to a large number of people, including those engaged in fishing, boat construction, gear production, processing, and marketing. Simultaneously small-scale operations are substantially increasing fish production, which is the cheapest source of animal protein in India, and this can be made available in increasing quantities to a wider sector of the population" (George 1973).

Conference Chairman A. W. H. Needler included this emphasis on social benefits in his Conference summary, noting that "support of the so-called artisanal fisheries, the small-boat fisheries . . . has high priority . . . It is clear that in the minds of most participants the welfare of the people is the most compelling objective" (Needler 1973).

In a very real sense, a society's socioeconomic character molds its fisheries management values and therefore delimits its goals. The industrialized affluent society provides the educational and other cultural advantages that nurture a conservation ethic—a sense of custodianship for the world's resources as well as a sober recognition that renewable resources must be harvested within limits of sustainable yield. That same society frees its citizens from near-total preoccupation with subsistence living, and opens the opportunity to devote time, energy, and wealth to the pursuit of recreational and other aesthetic values. If that society operates under a free enterprise system, it also requires that fisheries management goals include the nurturing of economic viability in the commercial fishing and fish-processing industry.

While it is useful to understand that our diversified fisheries goals and values are a product of our way of life, it is more pragmatically important to recognize that a reverse cause-and-effect relationship also operates. A society shapes the quality of life of its citizens by the resource management goals it accepts and then converts into public policy. Recognition of this pervasive impact of fisheries management policy suggests sources of strength for public action that we have not as yet effectively employed.

For example, when we seek to save the salmon fisheries of the Pacific Northwest from further destruction by foreign fishing or through river damming and other habitat degradations, our goal is not solely to assure the future of the commercial fishing industry and its products or to sequester salmon for the enjoyment of anglers. Additionally we are seeking continuance of a particular quality of life in the Pacific Northwest, a quality which benefits not only local citizens but all others who visit that favored area, and all who earn a living by serving those visitors. Tourism is the second most valuable industry in Oregon. How much of Oregon's attraction for tourists depends upon the special quality of life of its coastal and river port communities, its picturesque harbors and busy fishing fleets? How great would be the values foregone if the resource on which those fleets depend were diminished significantly or destroyed?

Optimum sustainable yield, or better stated, optimum utilization of the resource, has its most pervasive and perhaps most important application in influencing the quality of life now and for the future. The values we choose to optimize, translated into regulations for fisheries management, not only will shape the structure of our fisheries, but also will mold the character of our communities and of the people that comprise them.

In final analysis, political leaders must make the hard choices. Which of several competing demands for a limited fishery resource are most in the public interest? Which best hold options open for future choices? Therefore what priorities should be assigned both to resources management activities and resource allocation?

To increase the probability that these choices will be rational rather than emotional, professional fisheries biologists, economists, sociologists, engineers, lawyers, and administrators must combine their particular attitudes, skills, and techniques to produce an interdisciplinary factual foundation. For this process to be effective, fisheries scientists and management agencies must organize to facilitate the interdisciplinary dialog necessary, and state and federal governments must generate the necessary political will to act on the advices given. The concluding section to this paper offers some tentative suggestions for achieving these goals.

Institutional Organization for Multiple Use Fisheries Management— A Summary of Provisional Recommendations

The Fisheries Biologist: His Commitment to Management of Fisheries for Multiple Use Purposes

For reasons this symposium has underscored and documented, the fisheries biologist must recognize the reality of multiple use demands on most fishery resources, the consequent necessity that those fisheries be managed to satisfy diverse goals, and the requirement that multidisciplinary attitudes, skills, and methods be incorporated into the research and management process. Achievement of this rationale requires several intellectual exercises:

1. Recognition that for fisheries subject to multiple use, self-imposed restriction of professional purview to MSY is:

(a) something of a "cop-out," by definition avoiding consideration of other presumably valid demands on the resource;

(b) operationally self-defeating, since many practical management decisions require recognition of alternative values, uses, and demands;

(c) therefore ultimately destructive of advisory credibility on fisheries matters, since this self-limited scope of concern infers intellectual tunnel vision with respect to real world needs and values.

2. Acceptance of a full array of interdisciplinary goals as a composite objective for fisheries management. This array must include:

(a) objectives concerned with maintenance of resources, including sustainable yield, prevention of waste, and protection and enhancement of environmental productivity (cf. Alverson and Paulik 1973);

(b) objectives concerned with economic efficiency and maximizing the economic yield consistent with protection of the resource (cf. Gulland and Robinson 1973);

(c) objectives concerned with attainment of educational, recreational, aesthetic, and other social benefits relating to the quality of life (cf. Alverson and Paulik 1973; McKernan 1972).

3. Personal and professional commitment to development of the cross-disciplinary dialogs and other interactions necessary for interdisciplinary resolution of fisheries problems.

The Fisheries Management Agency: Institutional Arrangements to Facilitate Multiple Use Fisheries Management

To achieve these objectives, fisheries agencies should continue to extend their capabilities for actively shaping public attitudes and guiding formulation of public policy. This effectiveness is in part a product of the role the agency seeks for itself, either as an active formulator of public opinion and advisor on public policy, or as a relatively passive instrument for carrying out directives generated by others. Effectiveness also depends directly on public confidence in the professional competence of the scientific staff.

Institutional arrangements for facilitating multiple use fisheries management should include:

1. Attainment of an expanded public mandate for agency action, to include economic and social benefit goals as well as those relating to protection of the resource.

2. Consolidation of all research and management functions encompassed by this expanded mandate within a single department or other operational entity.

3. Organization of multidisciplinary teams as operational units for fisheries research and management.

(a) These teams should include full-time economists and ecologists as well as fishery biologists.

(b) Each team should be assigned the long-range task of developing a comprehensive fishery management plan to include: (1)

determination of actual and potential values of the resource; (2) researches relevant to management for multiple use; (3) evaluation of alternative management processes; and (4) recommendations for management action based upon all other elements of the study.

4. Development of personnel policies and practices which provide recruitment, retention, promotion, and other incentives as recognition for scientific competence of staff generally, and for achievements in interdisciplinary cooperative action particularly.

State Governments and the Political Will for Action

Fisheries agencies and their scientists can provide leadership and professional guidance toward rational multiple use management of fisheries. However, in a democratic society, only the people, acting through their political leaders, can convert the optimum yield idea from abstract concept to concrete action. This requires first a political will for that action, and second, effective institutional arrangements for implementation. At State levels, these should include the following:

1. A clear declaration of fisheries resource use policy as basis for management[1] and its

_____

[1] In 1970 the California Legislature approved such a policy statement as Section 1700 of the Fish and Game Code. This section states (in part): "It is hereby declared to be the policy of the state to encourage the conservation, maintenance, and utilization of the living resources of the ocean and other waters under the jurisdiction of the state for the benefit of all the citizens of the state . . . This policy shall include the following objectives: (a) The maintenance of sufficient populations of all species of aquatic organisms to assure their continued existence. (b) The recognition of the importance of the aesthetic, educational, scientific, and nonextractive recreational uses of the living resources of the California Current. (c) The maintenance of a sufficient resource to support a reasonable sport use where a species is the object of sport fishing, taking into consideration the necessity of regulating individual sport fishery bag limits to the quantity that is sufficient to provide a satisfying sport. (d) The growth of local commercial fisheries, consistent with aesthetic, educational, scientific, and recreational uses of such living resources, the utilization of unused resources, taking into consideration the necessity of regulating the catch within the limits of maximum sustainable yield . . ."

implementation through appropriately mandated action.

2. Close coordination and, where feasible, consolidation of fisheries research and management into a single operational entity based on the resource to be managed (rather than separation by user groups or type of operational function).

3. Development of funding for fisheries research and management which distributes the burden equitably among all who benefit (e.g., recreational, commercial, and nonextractive public beneficiaries).

4. Extension of cost benefit analyses to encompass all public benefits from the resource, including the importance of fishing enterprises to the socioeconomic structure of the coastal zone, resultant social benefits to the individual, economic benefits to the region (e.g., via tourism), etc.

5. Cooperative interaction with other jurisdictions for joint management of shared resources.

6. Development of legal processes and other mechanisms for mitigating overcapitalization problems which, as consequence of the unowned property character of the resource, jeopardize the economic viability of many commercial fisheries.

The National Government: Support for State and Regional Management Action, and Consideration of International Implications of the OSY Concept

Most of the suggestions for action at state levels apply equally well at the federal level. Additionally, the federal government has certain coordinational and oversight prerogatives and capabilities with respect to the states, as well as responsibility for negotiation with other nations on Law of the Sea and other matters of international policy.

In the context of these special federal responsibilities, the following would materially assist the objectives set forth in this paper:

1. Development of appropriate national (and international) statements of policy for fisher-

ies resources use and management, and organization of national machinery to cooperate actively with the states in coordinated regional and national management programs, but without preemption or other derogation of existing state and regional programs of demonstrated effectiveness.

2. Refinement of United States policy with respect to the full utilization principle to provide reasonable protection for the option of a coastal nation to manage the harvest from selected fisheries within its extended jurisdiction zone at other than maximum sustainable yield levels, in order to realize alternative values and permit alternative uses of those resources in the public interest.

Literature Cited

ALVERSON, DAYTON L., AND G. L. PAULIK. 1973. Objectives and problems of managing aquatic living resources. J. Fish. Res. Board Can. 30: 1936–1947.

BLACKBURN, MAURICE. 1969. Conditions related to upwelling which determine distribution of tropical tunas off western Baja California. U.S. Fish Wildl. Serv. Fish. Bull. 68(1): 147–175.

CONGRESSIONAL RECORD. February 7, 1973. Senate Concurrent Resolution 11—Submission of a concurrent resolution relating to the U.S. fishing industry. 119(22): S 2280-S 2282.

———. December 19, 1973. Senate Resolution 222—Submission of a resolution to authorize a National Ocean Policy study. 119(200): S 23315-S 23318.

CRUTCHFIELD, JAMES A., ed. 1965. The fisheries—problems in resource management. University of Washington Press, Seattle, Wash. 136 p.

GEORGE, P. C. 1973. Experience and plans for rationalization of small-scale fisheries in India. J. Fish. Res. Board Can. 30: 2172–2177.

GULLAND, J. A., AND M. A. ROBINSON. 1973. Economics of Fishery Management. J. Fish. Res. Board Can. 30: 2042–2050.

MANACOP, PORFIRIO R. 1953. The life history and habits of the goby, Sicyopterus extraneus Herre (Anga) Gobiidae with an account of the goby-fry fishery of Cagayan River, Oriental Misamis. Philippine J. Fish. 2(1): 1–60.

MCKERNAN, DONALD L. 1972. Science and politics in national fishery management. Pages 111–114 in Progress in Fishery and Food Science. Univ. Wash. Publ. Fish. New Ser. 5.

MESSERSMITH, JAMES D. 1969. Anchovy—small fish, big problem. Outdoor California. 30(5): 1–3.

———, JOHN L. BAXTER, AND PHILIP M. ROEDEL. 1969. The anchovy resources of the California Current region off California and Baja California. Calif. Mar. Res. Comm., Calif. Ocean. Fish. Invest. Rept. 13: 32–38.

NATIONAL ADVISORY COMMITTEE ON OCEANS AND ATMOSPHERE. 1973. Second annual report to the President and the Congress. 47 p.

NEEDLER, A. W. H. 1973. Chairman's summary of the highlights of the Conference. FAO Techical Conference on Fishery Management and Development. J. Fish. Res. Board Can. 30: 2508–2511.

PACIFIC MARINE FISHERIES COMMISSION. 1974. 26th Annual report of the Pacific Marine Fisheries Commission for the year 1973. p. 14–15, 26.

PINKAS, LEO, MALCOLM S. OLIPHANT, AND INGRID L. K. IVERSON. 1971. Food habits of albacore, bluefin tuna, and bonito in California waters. Calif. Dept. Fish and Game, Fish. Bull. 152: 10.

PROUDE, P. D. 1973. Objectives and methods of small-scale fisheries development. J. Fish. Res. Board Can. 30: 2190–2195.

STEVENSON, J. R. 1971. Submission of draft articles on the breadth of the territorial sea, straits and fisheries. U.S. Info. Serv., U.S. Mission. Geneva, August 3, 1971. 9 p.

———. 1974. An address before the plenary session of the Law of the Sea Conference. Mar. Fish. Rev., 36(8): 1–4.

UNITED NATIONS GENERAL ASSEMBLY. 1971. Draft articles on the breadth of the territorial sea, straits, and fisheries submitted by the United States. Doc. A/AC. 138/SC II/L.4. 30 July 1971. Pages 241–245 in Report of the Committee on the peaceful uses of the sea-bed and the ocean floor beyond the limits of national jurisdiction. 26th sess., Sup. 21 (A/8421).

Pacific Marine Fisheries Commission, 342 State Office Building, 1400 S.W. Fifth Avenue, Portland, Oregon 97201

Panel Discussion

Views of a State Fisheries Administrator

Thomas L. Linton

It is my great hope that this symposium produces results that are substantive instead of only semantic. Some of the problems that must be solved and some of the shortcomings that must be overcome are:

1. Fisheries biologists are often reluctant to give a definite answer because until they have the perfect sample, which consists of having all the specimens "pickled" (i.e., scale samples, length-frequency samples, etc.), they can't really be sure.

2. Biometricians also seek the perfect sample for population studies in order to have the irrefutable equation that will give the infallible curve.

3. Fishery administrators desire a program that will please all user groups and fulfill all political considerations.

4. User groups each desire to have all the fish for their excusive use (probably it is more accurate to say for each individual's use).

5. Resource economists most commonly continue to plug away at their age-old undertaking of arranging the externalities on the deck of the great ship Titanic, instead of addressing "real world" situations.

6. Enforcement programs are negotiated by the committee that was given the mission of designing a horse but ended up producing a camel. This has resulted in statutes, rules, and regulations based not upon fact, but upon superstition, mores, or pressure politics.

Fishery science and fishery scientists, I therefore conclude, are in one hell of a shape.

All of the presentations have directly stated or alluded to the principle of limited entry. I hope you are fully aware of the potentially volcanic eruption that may ensue from the commercial fishing sector if this concept is pursued to the point that its implementation

is attempted. Even to contemplate the effects of adopting a policy that only a certain number may sport fish does not insure long service with an agency. Aside from this mundane consideration, there is the constitutional question to be considered.

There are problems in the fisheries field that may require limited entry programs for both sport and commercial fishermen. These are the hard questions that face us. I wonder if we are bold enough to face the issue and willing to make the stand.

In an attempt to comply with the format of this symposium, I will respond to the points raised by the speakers, I would like to give my reaction to their major points from the standpoint of a state fishery agency administrator.

Dave Wallace raised the point of "quality." This is an area with which many agencies, my own included, have wrestled. Wallace's reference to the quality "sportfishing experience" and the need for a quality commercial fish product states two necessary objectives. However, both need to be quantified. The maximum sustainable yield concept may have the flexibility to provide the needed quantification for a part of the answer but not all. This problem, along with others, should not be viewed simply as the result of a faulty concept, although this may be true. As Wallace points, out, we have a serious lack of adequate institutional arrangements for implementation and enforcement of our fishery programs, particularly where other nations are involved.

Last, I heartily concur with the suggestion Wallace makes that we must take into account various factors, such as economic, social, and biological ones, when estimating optimum levels of harvest. The program should have the maximum flexibility possible because the factors listed above are variable and the program must be capable of responding to this variability.

Dr. Royce has very succinctly assembled and described the modeling "tools" available for use in the fisheries trade. By pointing out the strengths and shortcomings of these standard modeling techniques, he set the stage for the discussion here today. A further benefit of the presentation is the listing and discussion of the additional outputs from yield models that may be valuable in fishery negotiations beyond those relating to maximum sustainable yield. His suggestion of maximization of benefits appears to me to be a desirable goal, one that a manager must strive to achieve.

Professor Crutchfield, in his opening remarks, refers to his sadness in approaching his topic today. That sadness comes from the "tremendous accomplishments of fishery scientists" and "such limited results in the important area of public policy." I am reminded of the comment, "We don't know where we are going but we are making good time." It appears to me that if we are not successful in getting into practice programs that are related to conservation in some sense—be it biological, economic, social, etc.—instead of those that "reflect the accumulated effects of successive piecemeal retreats from sound management in the face of pressure from one group of fishermen, processors, or users against another," we cannot justify our efforts and our existence.

Crutchfield's point that only a small portion of the total fishery research effort is devoted to analysis that would yield answers of potential use to policy makers is all too often true. Having had an opportunity to be on both sides of this fence, it is a point of paritcular interest to me. There is no malice intended by either side, but a mutual lack of appreciation of each other's problems and pressures ("I'm not going to let some ivory-towered professor run my agency" *vs* " 'They' are not interested in scientific data because everything in that agency is politically motivated"). To establish the necessary continuing dialogue, the proper atmosphere of understanding should be a major objective.

This, coupled with Crutchfield's point that the fishery scientist and economist have the "humble task of moving management in the direction of a greater net economic benefit," will most probably give us "gains in human welfare" that I hope we are working toward (i.e. jobs, liveable wage, and improved standard of living).

The sortie by Crutchfield into international and recreational fishing matters, usually unpredictable, controversial and hostile territory, may be overly optimistic. Allocating a common property resource in the international arena in a fair and equitable way, getting an equal value for what is given, will test the metal of our shrewdest Yankee trader. Then, to develop peace and harmony between the commercial and sport fishermen (or even among sport fishermen) by rearrangement of fishing times and areas to minimize the "conflicts" may not be sufficient, given the well known "fact" that the best fishing is always over there where the other guy is fishing.

Professor Crutchfield's outline of the resource economists' "second best" program would, in my opinion, be a strong underpinning for fisheries management programs. Although he states this approach is for the commercial utilization of fishery resources, it appears to me this framework could also be applied to sport fishing. Even though the data economists desire are not readily available, this framework seems to provide a defensible guide for limiting the sport fishing take.

The evaluation of the sport fishing economic benefit by Radovich appears faulty in its logic. First, if we follow his line of reasoning, using as a gauge the total cost involved for all those attending this conference, then our meeting here today is of greater value to fishery science than our work back home! Second, the evaluation might have the effect of stopping farming efforts, because a big bunch of rich folks hunt deer, quail, or ducks, and farming activities take game land out of this use category. Managing in response to what could be termed social feelings, admirable though it may sound, might only be a cover term for what in fact is yielding to political pressure. To manage for social needs, however, is another matter. In my opinion, to give a more dependable program, we need objectives clearly stated and clearly understood. This provides a more justifiable case, and one capable of withstanding the tests imposed through biological, socio-economic, and political considerations.

Anderson's example concerning use of regulations for the production of good bass fishing corresponds to the point about the vital role of regulations and their enforcement that Dave Wallace made. Regulations, based on evidence rather than emotion, and enforcement of these regulations, must be a major part of the fish management strategy for any single or multi-species management program. And, as Anderson notes, in aquatic ecosystem management, "You can't stop at the water's edge." This is a more sensible approach. It underlies the need for a comprehensive and enforced land use management system. Water and land must be managed as a unit and not as separate entities.

Carlton advocates extension of the coastal jurisdiction, an action that has been taken by the North Carolina Legislature. We, as well as numerous other states that have already taken this action, consider this more as a signal to the federal government than as a corrective measure. Extension of United States jurisdiction, we theorize, provides for bargaining from a greater position of strength in the Law of the Sea Conference. This type of new commitment to protection of our fish stocks is very much needed and I concur with this suggestion. Further, his call for the establishment of a "rational use pattern" for the fish stocks, states a desirable goal. The road to that destination is not clearly mapped in my mind. One sure way to miss that goal is to continued behind the age-old cry that we need more research and more data. I heartily concur with Carlton that we do, in fact, have enough data for a great number of species to manage a fishery. New studies and continued studies are oftentimes a diversionary or delaying tactic. Believe me, I know because I have used that tactic.

And last but not least, Carlton's point about better public relations and support for fish management programs from the public strikes a responsive chord with me. Far too often, the fishery scientist is the world's worst public relations man. This must be corrected.

Harville proposed that the surplus from one nation be made available for harvest by another nation. This proposition has a good sound but I wonder if it is possible.

Aside from his bad joke at the beginning of his talk, Bob Mauermann made, in my estimation, an outstanding presentation. It conveys to me the impression of a man who has "been there." His plea for flexibility, illustrated by the black drum-channel bass controversy, surely must bring to mind many real life experiences that we all have had. The point it makes to me is that our track record with the public, in the courts, and with the politicians is pretty bad.

The panelists have led us through a number of considerations relating to fisheries matters at the local, national, and international level. Consideration of biological, socio-economic, and political factors, and their implications to fisheries management, was provided by the majority of the speakers. The search for a conceptual framework that would include these three levels and the three factors, I feel, used maximum *vs* optimum sustainable yield as simply a point of departure. The items listed by the various panelists as important ingredients—flexibility, management using existing data, management that does not stop at the water's edge, institutional arrangements for implementation and enforcement—could fit into available institutional systems.

Such a system could be found in a continuation of an expanded version of the very successful Aid to Research and Development in Commercial Fisheries (Public Law 88-309). The proposed program I make reference to is the state-federal partnership which is, in my opinion, simply an expansion of the 88-309 program, with the inclusion of the vitally important sport fishing industry. Implementing the state-federal partnership in conjunction with the pending "Interim Fisheries Zone Extension and Management Act of 1973" (S-1988) and the "High Seas Fisheries Conservation Act of 1973" (H.R. 4760) would be extremely beneficial to fisheries management. Whether this program is applied under maximum sustainable yield or optimum sustainable yield philosophy is a problem to be worked out later. The important point is that they be employed. They must be employed with adequate flexibility to make them useable tools within an institutional framework that will allow implementation and enforcement. If this can be done, we will have an optimum situation and probably an optimum sustainable yield. This should result in a program that would promote sound fisheries management.

Office of Marine Affairs, North Carolina Department of Administration, Raleigh, North Carolina   27603

Panel Discussion

Views of an Economist in the Academic World

Salvatore Comitini

I am glad to say Dr. Crutchfield's paper closely conforms to what I have to say about the economics of fisheries management. My basic opinion of the management problem is that it has both a biological and an economic aspect.

The biological aspect centers on finding that level of fishing effort which will maintain the stock and its yield at an optimum level. This, typically, has meant maximum sustainable yield (MSY), and it has usually been accomplished through some sort of regulation, as in quotas, closed seasons, yield restrictions, and devices of that sort. However, there is no way in a biological sense that we can say that a particular size of stock or yield is actually optimum.

Therefore, we need some way of valuing this optimum, or injecting a value system into it, to identify alternatives. Here is where the economist enters into the picture. The fishery actually is among what has traditionally been called by economists common property resources, meaning that there is free and open access to those resources. The right to exploit fishery resources is free, in contrast to other natural resource industries. This means that there is no way of limiting entry of effort such as would occur in other natural resource industries, which typically come under the ownership or management of an entrepreneur or a state.

So, what happens in a fishery is that generally you get too many vessels, too much labor, too much capital invested in exploiting the resource, which eventually threatens it with depletion. I have heard some speakers, this morning and this afternoon, assert that the objective of maximum sustainable yield has not done very much to improve fisheries. This is probably because this objective, by itself, is not adequate for optimal results.

What are some of the objectives of fishery management? The maximum sustainable yield objective would be feasible only where there is one stock, one method of catching that stock. However, usually there are choices between species and methods of catching those species. You can not catch all species simultaneously. This is the biggest objection to maximum sustainable yield.

The maximum economic yield is generally not vulnerable to this type of criticism. Everybody agreed that it was desirable to prevent unnecessary waste of labor and capital. Also, by placing values on different species of fish, and costs on different fishing methods, you can decide which combination of fishing activity would maximize the net economic yield.

However, there are some difficulties with the net economic yield objective, as has been agreed. How do we exclude excess factors in production that are already engaged in the fisheries, without running into the political and social problems involved? Another difficulty is that there are different choices that may be made by different countries who are exploiting the same fisheries resources. Some countries may want to catch small size fish, other countries, large size fish.

We may want to protect the fur seal fishery or the fur seal industry. That might also apply to the salmon fishery. It depends on what the main preferences are and what valuations are placed on labor and capital by the different countries. Take, for example, the Pacific Northwest conflict between Japan, the United States, and Canada. Japanese fishermen trawl for cod, which is a bottom fishery resource. They generally catch large amounts of halibut. To the United States and Canada, halibut is more important than cod. The Japanese place a relatively high valuation on cod and are generally excluded from fishing halibut. Here, you get a conflict between demand preferences and methods of fishing.

So you have these conflicts even with the maximum economic yield objective. How do you reconcile these? We may have two possible solutions to this problem. If you have a world market for fish, then, based on world prices and costs, the various countries would decide what species they want to catch and export to the highest value market, dividing up the revenues among themselves. This would make the world better off, although the problem is that we do not have a world market for fish.

Generally, we have trade barriers between countries and barriers to the movement of labor and capital. Therefore, we do not have one market for one type of fish. Values and costs differ between countries. However, Dr. Crutchfield pointed out that you can divide an international fishery resource between countries, by allocating national quotas and allowing each country to exploit its quota separately. This seems to work with some species, such as the relatively immobile species in the Northwest Atlantic, which have a barrier to movement. But, it would be very difficult to allocate those resources which are highly mobile, such as tuna, and resources which are closely interrelated with each other. So, how do you get around these possible problems? Well, since the net economic yield objective seems to be generally more satisfactory than the maximum sustained yield objective, in view of the difficulties in management, there is a question of developing workable guidelines for decision-making.

It is now time to work towards the closest consensus that is possible regarding the choice of species, the choice of methods of fishing, the choice of level of catches, level of effort, etc. Also included in the decision criteria must be some of the political and social and historical considerations, which many of the people who have previously spoken have included in their optimum sustainable yield objective. Also, we can devise agreements which make world users better off than does their next best course of action. It is like a second-best solution. That is, we can determine how much better off everybody is with a management regime than without a management regime. And the benefits among these alternatives can be divided up so that everybody is better off than without the management regime.

Now sitting here this morning and this afternoon, I have heard a great deal of discussion dealing with OSY (optimum sustainable yield) and MSY. The distinction between the two positions, it seems to me, is that OSY proponents apparently want to inject social and political considerations, in addition to economic considerations, into the management objective. However, we still have to have some control over effort to obtain the optimum sustainable yield objective. The question is how is it done? We still have to know what the relative costs and benefits are between these choices in order to determine the OSY objective. OSY lies somewhere in between MSY and the maximum net economic yield on the cost-benefit curve. The choice as to where you want to be on the curve depends on maximizing some net benefits, however you want to define them, including the political and social criteria.

Another aspect of the OSY regime is what it does to the role of the economist. For the economist, rather than defining *the* optimum objective, such as maximum economic yield, all he would do is simply state the costs of an alternative course of action, within an OSY framework. So, we still have to think in terms of maximizing something. When you think about it in terms of cost, in terms of the optimum sustainable yield objective, you still have to think in terms of maximum net benefit. Thus, in the last analysis, we are back again to maximizing something in some form or another.

Department of Economics, University of Hawaii at Manoa, 2424 Maile Way, Honolulu, Hawaii 96822

Panel Discussion

Views of a Recreational Fisherman

Frank L. Cassidy, Jr.

It is a pleasure to be here, first to hear remarks from all segments of our industry and our resources, as well as scientific remarks and economic remarks, from both federal and state personnel. To put it bluntly, I think we have problems.

I paused briefly after I said that to see whether anyone fell off his chair, or if we began to sink slowly out of sight. Neither of those things happened and neither of them will, because the fact that we have problems is not new to any of us. It did occur to me today that no one said that we didn't have problems, and that is an interesting point worth thinking about. Not one presentation today indicated there is no problem in the fisheries resources.

The problem, in my words, is that we learn too quickly and we are seldom satisfied, particularly in regard to our fisheries techniques. I think we are overutilizing our marine resources, and I do not mean only commercial fisheries. I mean all aspects, commercial, recreational, management, some scientific, some economic. It is obvious to me that, given time, perhaps a shorter time than we might imagine, we can totally fish out specific parts of our marine resource, if not all our marine resource.

When I think about that prospect, fishing out parts of it or all of it, I feel there in fact lies our answer. If it were all gone, we could get together a combined force of the Soil Conservation Service, the Corps of Engineers, the Forest Service, and the Departments of Interior, Agriculture, and Commerce, and undertake a restoration project. That is really what we are best at, unfortunately, in dealing with so many other problems of our environment. I'm teasing you. I don't think that is a correct answer and neither do you.

The resource is badly depleted in many areas for a variety of reasons. Some were discussed here, some were not. The underlying reason, particularly evident from the presentations today, is that we have what I would consider to be lack of preventive management. We fail to prevent fishermen from exceeding the allowable catch.

Call it MSY, OSY, or ABC or whatever, if we agree that a problem exists, and I think we do, and we know it has existed for some time, what should we do about it? My recommendation is that we undertake immediately, as soon as today if possible, to begin a scientific program of species-oriented management systems. This should be the guide to maintenance of abundant resources for all times as the overall objective, within which the commercial fisheries and the recreational fisheries must stand or fall.

This management scheme should consider the welfare of fish, first and foremost. That would not be a very popular objective. It would be a painful change in philosophy for a lot of the management personnel at both federal and state levels. Some element of every part of the industry, commercial or recreational, would voice violent objections. Specifically, the commercial fishery on some species should be cut back or curtailed completely. Specifically, some parts of the recreational fishing should be cut back or curtailed completely. Foreign nations must be put on immediate notice of our main intentions and the forcefulness with which we intend to implement them and to pursue that management policy.

Coordinated management between state and federal agencies and perhaps even some city and county aspects, should be implemented and maintained in good faith. Now those are two important words, "good faith." What do they mean? I'll give you an example of what I consider to be the need for good faith.

In my state of Washington, we have one section of the Department of Interior that is helping us fund the management of our steelhead resources, in terms of monitoring catch, etc. At the same time, we have another section of the Department of Interior lobbying for funds to create hatcheries on Indian reservations, which another section of the Department of Interior supports and which operate totally out of the control of our management system. This is the type of confusion we want to avoid. I am not discrediting or devaluing either one of the programs. Both are good and both can be useful, but they are not coordinated. They could be very unuseful and certainly unscientific and not in "good faith."

The recreational fishery must be promoted on the "experience" level rather than the catch level, as was brought out somewhat mildly here in a couple of different presentations. This promotion has to be undertaken by all of us, because I doubt that there is any way that you can prove to me economically or scientifically that recreational fishermen go fishing for meat. I know that with photographic equipment, and many other things, we can promote an experience level of fishing second to none, if we work at it.

It has been proven to me that anglers do not go fishing for the meat. Let me give you an example. I am a steelhead fisherman by hobby. I enjoy the fine streams of southwest Washington, where I live, with my father who is retired and has always wanted to catch a steelhead. It took him eight years to get his first fish, eight years of arduous work in which he bought a $4,000 boat, an $1,800 motor, a $5,000 International Travellall to tow it, and at least an additional $500 in accumulated gear. After this investment he caught one eight-pound fish. Now, I want to make it clear, that's $1,400 a pound of fish caught, anyway you look at it, which is hardly fishing for the meat!

Another important thing that has to be recognized is that the recreational fisheries interests, who desperately want a bigger voice in the management of the marine resources, must be prepared to pay their way. I would like to see a fee of some kind, be it to fund either state or federal management. If sportsmen want a voice in management, they have to put up some of the muscle and invest the "bucks." It is time they did in some respects. It has always bothered me that in my fine state of Washington you can fish for salmon without paying a single cent. And that doesn't really give me much confidence, when I try to speak today as a sportsman, that the value of sport fishing does exist.

Another point occurs to me. I think it's time that the sportsman and the commercial fisherman get together to reunify their effort towards the original objective of maintenance of the resource. We can no longer afford the petty infighting and back-biting that goes on at virtually every meeting that I attend. I would like to compliment the people here because it hasn't happened at this Symposium, and that is a real credit to the quality of people attending.

Many people reduce themselves to bitter battles about how best to catch the fish, and to whom they belong, and who pays for them, between the federal and state governments, between sportsmen and commercials. Gentlemen, I just think we have no time for that any longer. I think it is time to unify and get on a common course to resolve the problems of the resources and maintain them. I think it is also time we admitted that it is not a crime to leave an extra fish in the pasture. I don't advocate waste; that is ridiculous. It is not smart, it is not good business sense, and it is not good economic sense. I feel that our management systems that advocate harvesting all possible fish, while leaving just enough to regenerate for the next onslaught, have helped to put us where we are now, I think that putting an extra fish in the pasture, without creating economic waste, would be sensible.

Now, what will happen if some of these things are implemented? Again, I don't want to shock any of you into a fainting spell, but, I think that probably, with good luck, the commercial fishermen will survive and will survive profitably, particularly those who practice sound management. And that is what the system is all about, sound management. It begets more profit, which is what makes our capitalistic society work.

My business is in building materials supply, particularly with the many contractors who build on-site residential homes. I am finding that sound management is a pretty good thing to have. I can remember many of my unsound management competitors who aren't around any more. That should be the case with every industry, and I do not think the fishing industry is any exception.

The myth that the commercial fishing industry exists because it supplies vitally needed protein you can get nowhere else, has been destroyed, particularly today. I thought Dr. Crutchfield did a good job of explaining the alternative approaches to provision of protein through many measures, probably cheaper, probably with less investment, but not designed to satisfy the particular tastes of our people. I think, too, that if these things are applied, the recreational fisherman can pursue his "experience," pursue it enjoyably within the framework of maintaining the resources for all times. Also I think we will emerge as a world leader in developing and maintaining our oceanic "hatcheries" and resource, and be no less popular than we are now.

I want to mention one other thing that happened in these last two weeks that should be of interest in reference to what we are doing now and the talk we have heard about the demands on the resource for meeting world protein requirements. There was a population conference held during the last two weeks. The United States and several other countries went to that conference with the hope of drafting an acceptable resolution providing for some form of population control.

All the ideas for any kind of population control, or population management of any kind, were soundly defeated. In fact, the problem is that most countries will not even admit there is a problem, although we are headed towards doubling ourselves in thirty-five years. I predict that our ability to raise food and provide a source of food for the world will be as powerful a factor in our ability to influence world problems as any nuclear capability we might develop. I would also reiterate, perhaps as the most important comment I picked up today, one that is seldom made, that not only should we educate ourselves, we should take on the responsibility of educating the uneducated. Too often people in conservation or the fishing industries end up meeting like we did today and telling each other that we have problems.

Admitting that we have problems and coming up with resolutions and solutions, we think that our work is done. That mistake is made in labor movements, in religion, and in every stratum of our society. Our job is to tell the people who do not know about the problems what is going on. I call it going to Cedar Rapids, Iowa, and convincing the local legislator that he has problems in his fishery resources. If we can do that, then we are going to direct the proper attention towards the problem. I predict, flatly, that if we do not initiate some action now, the problem will solve itself, which is what I consider the most expensive solution of all.

Son Sales, Ltd., 1020 North West Front Avenue, Portland, Oregon 97209

Panel Discussion

Usefulness of the Optimum Yield Concept

Richard S. Croker

As made clear by today's speakers, "optimum sustainable yield" can be described as a deliberately imprecise term coined to please everyone. You have noticed that no two speakers have described it exactly the same, and if *they* are confused, imagine how puzzled a layman would be. In spite of its inexact nature and the impossibility of ever achieving a yield at anywhere near optimum level in actual practice, the concept has a lot going for it.

The best thing about the term optimum yield is that it leaves all sorts of options open for everyone—the administrator, the scientist, the public, and every kind of fisherman. For each one of us can define the optimum yield of any fishery to suit ourself. The term includes a blending of every point of view—biological, political, economic, sociological, nationalistic, and idealistic. Everyone puts forth his or her view of what optimum means, they are all stirred up together, and the best points by everyone are considered. Then the viewpoint of whoever has the most political clout is declared to be "optimum." Whatever nation has the most power succeeds in imposing its kind of optimum on weaker countries. The processor, or commercial fisherman, or sportsman, or conservationist with the most votes gets to decide how the take will be apportioned. It's just like it has always been except that now we have a loftier sounding goal, and perhaps a more rational decision can be made.

In theory at least, both maximum sustainable yield and maximum economic yield can be more precisely determined. But they both have grave shortcomings, as noted by the speakers today. Not many species of fish or shellfish have been managed very successfully in the name of maximum sustainable yield, and maximum economic yield is seldom even considered. Such successes as we have had have been mostly due to luck. So far, the guy with the most power, whoever he may have been, has done as he damned well pleased, in spite of the best efforts of the likes of us gathered here.

The total result has been a dramatic decline in the stocks of the world's most valuable fisheries. At best we have only postponed the final day of reckoning while talking vaguely about marketing plankton and lantern fish and trash species to take the place of whales, tuna, salmon, and all the other high value species.

It is noteworthy and unfortunate that nearly all the speakers seemed to consider optimum yield in terms of fishing regulations only. Only one speaker stressed environmental factors and also mentioned artificial propagation. Except possibly in the case of strictly high seas species, these two factors are of at least equal importance in any discussion of optimum yield.

No matter how we define an optimum yield, it must be remembered that no fish species can produce any kind of optimum yield if its environment is meanwhile damaged. As we change our thinking from maximum to optimum, we must increase our emphasis on maintaining the environment or we will have no fisheries on which to set regulations.

Canada has taken a long step forward by establishing its Ministry of the Environment, recognizing that without a place to live no species of fish can survive to produce even a minimum yield. For the most part, the United States Government and the various states have not faced up to this concept wholeheartedly, perhaps for fear of slaying certain sacred cows.

To achieve an optimum yield, it is necessary in some cases to take advantage of modern fishcultural techniques to augment, replace, or substitute other species for, drastically reduced stocks. No longer is mariculture or aquiculture just a wildeyed dream. Although it is expensive, it is entirely feasible for many high-value species of fish and shellfish, freshwater, anadromous, and marine.

Resources management includes both regulation of catch and maintenance of the environment, with an assist from artificial propagation. The term optimum yield includes all three. In striving for optimum yield, let's not fall into the trap of blunting our spears on the nearly impossible task of conservation through regulation alone.

The big advantage of the word optimum is the variety of ways it can be defined. Ideally, it means the best for everyone, but in fisheries usage it will undoubtedly grow to mean something less. We all know that "conservation" means "wise use" and that wise use to most fishermen means "my use before someone else gets to use it." Optimum will go the same way.

To many, optimum yield will mean cutting in the sportfishermen on a larger share of the catch so the commercial fishermen don't get them all. Or maybe the reverse. Or it may mean cutting in one kind of commercial fisherman on harvests made principally by those using some other kind of gear. It can even restrict sportsmen to using only artificial lures or barbless hooks or whatnot. It may mean little or no consumptive use in order to rebuild a spawning stock, to protect an associated species, to provide forage for other species, or to enhance educational or recreational use which doesn't remove fish from the stock. Conversely it can mean temporary deliberate over-harvest of certain species to encourage other varieties or even to provide employment or food during emergencies.

You have noticed, perhaps, that since my first sentence I have omitted the word "sustainable" and have used "optimum yield" only. This was deliberate. For one thing optimum implies continuing, not temporary. Also sustainable connotes a rigidly level yield, and we all know that the catch has to go up or down from year to year because of many reasons, and optimum catch one season may be at a greatly different level than last or next year. I suggest that we leave out the word sustainable and call it simply Optimum Yield.

The awkward thing about all three kinds of yields—optimum, maximum and economic—is that they can be applied so much easier to single species fisheries than to the usual multi-species fisheries. Actually, nearly all fisheries include a variety of species, either where several kinds are fished for together deliberately, or where some kinds are taken incidentally to others, or where catching one variety has a real impact on the stock of an associated species. This multiplicity of species adds to the confusion because optimum for one kind is seldom optimum for all the others. It is necessary, then, to consider the whole assortment, which is easier to do if we think optimum. It is high time that the fisheries professional think in terms of the whole picture and discard the tunnel vision of single species thinking.

If optimum yield is a good concept, as I believe it is, something should be done about it besides talking. Accordingly, I am proposing that the American Fisheries Society undertake an action program to do the following:

(1) Consolidate all the thinking on the concept of optimum yield into a concise summary, listing the advantages and shortcomings of the concept for each kind of fishing. Until the concept has been described and justified in plain English it will never sell—to the fishery professional, the resource user, the decision maker, or the general public.

(2) Adopt a position on fishery research that will aim the research directly toward determining the optimum yield. As one of the speakers pointed out, we will never have the money, manpower, or time to learn every fact we want to on every species, so it will be necessary to concentrate on those lines of research that will lead to delineating optimum yield. Cut out the frills and make do with what we can get. Neither tell the world that we know everything or know nothing, but that the best facts available indicate that this is what can be done.

(3) Prepare a series of project reports on a variety of hypothetical fisheries, to be used

for demonstrating to U. S. and Canadian national, state, and provincial agencies how they might set up projects on actual fisheries. The reports will show step by step how the projects were conducted. Input will be provided by persons both within and outside the agencies, including fishery and oceanic or limnological scientists, administrators, economists, sociologists, politicians, and resource users: commercial and sport fishermen, and, where pertinent, nonconsumptive users.

(4) Each report will include a computer study that will list all possible options, indicating the effect on the resource, on the various users, and on the general public of every action that might be taken and how much each action would cost. By action, I mean the imposition of restrictive or liberalized regulations, steps to maintain or improve the environment, and artificial propagation. Conversely, negative steps will be programmed in, such as overexpansion of fishing effort and damage to the environment by outside agencies or individuals. Until we go into computer programmed models we will continue flying by the seat of our pants.

With this series of reports in hand, a management agency staff can more readily apply the best possible techniques to prepare an optimum yield study on whatever fishery has a problem. In actual practice, the decision-making authority will have the benefit of a wide spectrum of advice. It will be able to evaluate all its options. And everybody involved will have a pretty good idea of the consequences of any decision, good or bad. Perhaps best of all, the fishery professional will have a feeling of meaningful personal participation, something that is sadly lacking now.

31592 Crystal Sands Drive, Laguna Niguel, California 92677.

A Summary and Critique of the Symposium on Optimum Sustainable Yield

Philip M. Roedel

What seems like an eon ago, though actually it has been only seven years, I raised some questions about yield concepts during a talk opening a symposium. This was in 1967, and in that instance we were concerned with the abundance and potential of the living resources of the California Current System. The questions, which have changed very little in the intervening years, were these: What should guide us in establishing levels of exploitation: conventional maximum sustainable yield (MSY), "maximum sustainable economic yield," "maximum sociological yield" (that which would provide optimal recreational value), some combination thereof —or something else yet again? In essence, do we maximize in terms of kilograms or in terms of dollars? Or are we looking for some other measure at least with respect to certain sorts of fisheries? (Roedel 1969.)

These issues had been argued before and they have been argued since. Until today, I do not believe the proponents of various points of view have ever really gotten together in a serious attempt to define terms, debate issues, and attain understanding, if not agreement, on the use and validity of optimum sustainable yield (OSY) as a tool in fisheries management.

The discussions—controversies, if you will —of today concerning the principles of fisheries management and of the concept of MSY as the overriding criterion for harvest have a most familiar ring to those of use who were involved in California fisheries affairs in the 1960's. What happened was that a tremendous amount of interest in the ocean and in its resources developed in that state early in the decade.

In the years that followed, the issues that still plague us were debated at great length in various public forums—issues such as limited entry, allocations between sport and commercial interests, international allocations, the role of state and federal government, the role of the private sector, and, importantly, the criteria for management. What principles should cover allocations and what standards should govern harvest?

In 1965, the University of California published a report that is, so far as I can ascertain, the first major planning document for fisheries to give priority to aesthetic values and recreational resources, albeit within the framework of "maximizing the sustained harvest" as the objective of management. The implication is certainly there that this commitment to sport fishing would require some bending of a pure MSY concept.

The report (California University 1965), prepared under the direction of Dr. M. B. Schaefer, recommended that the State government should establish policy with respect to living resources that would include the following objectives:

To give priority to aesthetic and recreational uses in those cases where a species which is an object of sportfishing, and is under control of the State, is not capable of supporting the reasonable requirements of the sportfish harvest and the existing or potential commercial harvest;
To encourage the growth of local commercial fisheries, consistent with aesthetic, educational, scientific and recreational uses;
To manage, on a basis of adequate scientific information promptly promulgated for public scrutiny, the fisheries under the State's jurisdiction and to participate in the management of other fisheries in which California fishermen are engaged, with the objective of maximizing the sustained harvest and decreasing costs of commercial production.

The next year the California Department of Fish and Game picked up the sport fish priority in its Fish and Wildlife Plan (1966), added to it the concept (without defining it) of optimum yield and recognized economic factors.

The language is this:

> To manage marine resources for the optimum sustainable harvest giving priority to recreational uses where a species or species group under State jurisdiction is incapable of supporting both the reasonable requirement of the sport fishery and the existing or potential commercial harvest. Where the optimum sustainable harvest of a species or species group is insufficient to support both the recreational and commercial demand, first priority should be given to satisfying the reasonable and legitimate demands of the recreational fishery; the commercial fishery should be encouraged to use any harvestable surplus remaining after the recreational demand is satisfied.

The California legislature in 1970 codified this general concept of marine resource management in Section 1700 of the California Fish and Game Code (for the text, see Harville, *supra*, page 63).

The final legislation was a far cry from the Department's recommendation of optimum sustainable harvest, and certainly watered down the sportfishing priority. It does give statutory recognition to non-extractive values and retains an implied priority to sport over commercial fishing in some circumstances. The important thing is that the events leading to its passage got a lot of people thinking about rationales for management. That the "traditional" school prevailed is not surprising. What is surprising is that the idea of recognizing values other than commercial, with its down-stream implications for MSY, remained in.

The concepts of full utilization and MSY had most powerful backers then as they do today, including such giants in the field as Dr. W. M. Chapman. There was no question as to where he stood—strong and firm for MSY. In a 1970 paper, one of the last he wrote before his untimely death, he dismissed the concept of OSY in a footnote as a "confused term, attempting to combine the above two terms (net economic yield and MSY) unsuccessfully because they are incompatible."

While economists may have been the first to argue against MSY, they were not the last. Sportsmen came into the picture with their own definition of optimum yield and full utilization. The traditional economic argument was in the context of commercial fishing, and sportsmen are concerned more with quality. Optimum yield in the sense of maximum economic return was not necessarily what they wanted, but it came closer than MSY, which had far more negative implications.

The sportsmen's concept was more to the effect that catch quotas or allocations or yields should be set not on a purely biological or purely economic basis, but on a formula that somehow took both of these plus social factors into account, and further that full utilization was not necessarily synonymous with MSY. For example, there is the large relatively unexploited stock of anchovies off the coast of California and Baja California. The MSY has been estimated in the order of a million tons or more. So far as California sportsmen are concerned, none, or at the most a very small proportion, of this million tons should be harvested commercially. They believe that the anchovy resource is by their definition fully utilized as fodder for game fish and in small quantities as live bait for sport fishermen. In this case the optimum yield is close to no harvest. In other cases the optimum yield may be neither the maximum poundage nor the maximum dollars but the maximum number of fish that the stock can yield within the concept of satisfactory angling. You could call this subset of optimum yield the maximum social yield. This is, of course, the application of social and economic principles upon the biological, with the contention, which is probably true, that the social and economic benefits to the nation would be greater from a smaller poundage of such species as Pacific yellowtail taken by sportsmen than by commercial harvesting of the stock at MSY.

It is worth noting here that the primary motivation of sport fishermen is not necessarily to catch fish. John Radovich, in his presentation, cited Richard Bryan (1974) and I want to carry that reference a step further. Bryan's paper gave the results of what you might call a motivation study of British Columbia sportsmen. It has an intriguing title— "The dimensions of a salt-water sport fishing trip, or what do people look for in a fishing trip besides fish?" and a summary worth quoting a little more extensively:

This study has investigated in broad terms the variety of satisfactions which fishermen look for in a fishing trip. Few readers will be surprised that the harvesting aspect of fishing is relatively unimportant but more may be surprised that the catching aspect seems to be as well. The most important dimensions of a fishing trip for the surveyed fishermen were the escapism-relaxation and out-of-doors aspects of the activity. . . A minimum supply of fish sufficient to allow sport fishing is of course necessary. Trade-offs between increases in the supply of fish beyond this minimum and opportunities to augment the supply of other satisfaction generating components need to be carefully evaluated. At the level of primary motivation for a fishing trip it must be emphasized that 88 percent of the surveyed fishermen were seeking satisfactions unrelated to the catching or eating of fish. Consequently, fisheries managers who concentrate their energies exclusively on the supply of fish can be said to be managing fish production but they will certainly not be managing sport fish recreation.

Following this theme, Gary K. Bowen suggested at the 1974 Canadian Sport Fisheries Conference that "A reasonable objective for sport fisheries management should be to maximize the net satisfaction accruing to sportsmen" (conference document). He was, to quote again, "deliberately vague on the subject of an appropriate unit of measure." But this is all akin to the term suggested (only half facetiously) by a colleague in the National Marine Fisheries Service shortly after that organization rose from the ashes of the old Bureau of Commercial Fisheries. Faced with unfamiliar recreational demands and with the need to develop new standards for a new constituency, he proposed the MHQ —the maximum happiness quotient.

The increased interest in and support of a yield concept other than MSY has grown apace in recent years in biological, economic, and administrative thinking. Two recent nongovernmental actions attest to this. These are the resolutions adopted by the International Association of Game, Fish and Conservation Commissioners in 1973 and by the Sport Fishing Institute in 1974, both of which endorse the concept of optimum yield.[1]

This growing interest has not been reflected in official United States fisheries positions at international negotiating tables but is showing in Congressional actions.

Two bills are particularly noteworthy. On June 25, 1974, Representatives Sullivan, Dingell, and Biaggi introduced HR 15619, "The Fisheries Conservation Act of 1974," as a substitute for an Administration bill, HR 4760. In HR 4760, the Secretary of Commerce is authorized but not required to promulgate regulations that "will result in the optimum overall nutritional economic and social benefits." The new bill makes Secretarial action mandatory to bring about "the optimum overall biological, economic and social benefits."

A month later, on July 29, 1974, Senator Magnuson, on behalf of himself and others, introduced a completely revised version of S 1988, a bill that provides for interim extension of U.S. fisheries jurisdiction. The new draft speaks of optimum sustainable yield, which it defines as "the largest net return consistent with the biological capabilities of the stock, as determined on the basis of all relevant economic and environmental factors" [Sec. 3(11)].

The definition in the Senate Committee report which Chairman Stroud quoted in his opening statement uses somewhat more precise terminology: ". . . the largest net economic

---

[1] The operative paragraphs of these resolutions read as follows:

Now, THEREFORE BE IT RESOLVED, that the International Association of Game, Fish and Conservation Commissioners endorse a limited entry for commercial fishery that operates on the basis of quotas for harvestible stocks;
and
BE IT FURTHER RESOLVED, that the Association recommends that each state and province holding jurisdiction over the fish in its waters and the federal governments in coastal waters adopt a policy to assure the development of a system of optimum yields that will guarantee maximum public benefits incorporating both sport fishing and commercial food fishing values.

NOW, THEREFORE, BE IT RESOLVED, that the Board of Directors of the Sport Fishing Institute, assembled in regular annual meeting, May 16, 1974, at Corpus Christi, Texas, do herewith urge the state and federal fisheries agencies to revise their fisheries management concepts so as to better accommodate the needs of the recreational fisheries, as well as those of the commercial fisheries, by substituting the concept of optimum-yield management, in effect maximum economic yield, as needed replacement for the out-moded concept of maximum sustained yield.

return consistent with the biological capabilities of the stock, as determined on the basis of all relevant economic, biological and environmental factors."

Whether the omission of social benefits, which are specifically included in HR 15619, is significant I do not know. In any event, S 1988 in its original form talked only of maximum yield. Now, it speaks of optimum sustainable yield, as defined above, as the level not to be exceeded by the combined U.S. and foreign catch. The bill does not mention recreation specifically, as does HR 15619, but recreational fishing appears to be covered by the definition of fishing, and recreational input is not precluded and perhaps implied throughout.

So over the past two decades or so we have seen the emergence of economic theory with respect to commercial harvest, and the development of a point of view that quality is important and that priorities favoring non-commercial aspects are appropriate. This latter is, of course, nothing new. Without worrying about nuances, and without the benefits of sophisticated yield models, our history of fish and game management is that when sport and commercial groups have competed for the same species and the supply has been insufficient, or deemed insufficient, to fill the needs of both user groups, the species has been allocated to the sportsmen. The examples are almost endless. The market hunters for big game or for migratory waterfowl have long since passed from the scene and many species of fish, both inland and marine, are off the commercial list. This has been done by legislative action at both the state and federal levels.

Recreational yield is, by these actions, optimal yield. If it is also the maximum sustainable yield in a traditional sense, this is coincidence.

The International Perspective

In any discussion of yield concepts, we must take note of international viewpoints, and the subject has already been dealt with in varying degrees of detail. To recapitulate and to fill out the record, let me attempt to

answer this question: What has gone on and what is going on particularly in the Law of the Sea negotiations, and specifically where does the United States government stand?

The 1958 United Nations Conference on the Law of the Sea (LOS) is a good place to start. You can pursue the history of these concepts through many years before that, but the events are well documented and need not be repeated for our purposes.

Other speakers have cited the key language in Article 2 of the 1958 Fishing Convention.[2] It is worth looking at again:

As employed in this Convention, the expression "conservation of the living resoures of the high seas" means the aggregate of the measures rendering possible the optimum sustainable yield from those resources so as to secure a maximum supply of food and other marine products.

You have to read the whole sentence carefully, for it is the qualifier at its end that defines "optimum sustainable yield" to mean maximum physical production. And, as John Harville noted, maximum sustainable yield has remained a cornerstone of the United States fisheries position, together with its companion principle of full utilization.

Geneva 1958 was overtaken by events and in 1970, the United Nations embarked on a series of conferences preparatory to another formal LOS deliberation.

The United States introduced draft articles on the issues of breadth of the territorial sea, straits and fisheries on 30 July 1971 [United Nations General Assembly (UNGA) 1971]. With respect to yield concepts, it is simple and direct, calling for MSY, though "taking into account relevant environmental and economic factors."

Over the course of the next year the U.S. reevaluated its position and on 4 August 1972 submitted revised draft fisheries articles (UNGA 1972b) which, however, said essentially the same thing with respect to yield:

Conservation Principles

In order to assure the conservation of living marine resources, the coastal state or appropriate international organization shall apply the following principles:

_____

[2] Convention on Fishing and Conservation of the Living Resources of the High Seas, 17 UST 138, TIAS 5969, 559 UNTS 285.

Allowable catch and other conservation measures shall be established which are designed, on the basis of the best evidence available, to maintain or restore the maximum sustainable yield, taking into account relevant environmental and economic factors . . .

Ambassador Stevenson, the head of the United States delegation, said in a speech the next week (10 August 1972) that U.S. acceptance of broad coastal state jurisdiction over coastal and anadromous stocks was predicated in part on assurance of maximum yield from them.

Howard Pollock, Deputy Administrator of the National Oceanic and Atmospheric Administration, and senior Department of Commerce representative on the United States delegation, made a major address on 3 April 1973. Discussing a U.S. working paper dealing chiefly with tuna and salmon (UNGA 1973a), he emphasized the qualifications on MSY in the U.S. fisheries draft articles relating to the quality of the evidence and to the requirement for economic and environmental input. However, he in no way modified the U.S. position holding the MSY concept as fundamental.

So much for the official record, which stood unchanged when the Caracas session of LOS opened in June, 1974. Two unofficial comments on the United States position are worth noting. Both were made in 1973 by people thoroughly familiar with—and party to—many of the internal discussions of the U.S. delegation and its advisors. W. C. Herrington, Thomas Clingan, and Lowell Wakefield, in an article published in May, 1973, felt that "the stated objective 'maximum sustainable yield' is somewhat confining but the qualification, 'taking into account relevant environmental and economic factors' provides some leeway to consider economic and social as well as biological yields."

However, at last year's American Fisheries Society meeting (September 1973), Herbert Larkins of the National Marine Fisheries Service, who was on the U.S. team through the spring 1973 meeting, described our position as being quite conservative, in the sense of standing firm for the traditional biological interpretation of MSY. He said:

What we are seeking is a regime in which that part of the allowable catch not taken by the coastal state must be made available—under reasonable conditions of access—to foreign fishermen. This is the essence of the maximum utilization concept.

And later in the same talk:

. . . the concept of maximum utilization would not permit a coastal state to build up or maintain an accumulated stock for some future time when the high catch rates associated with an underutilized population could help defray the high initial costs of a budding fishery, nor would it allow the purposeful maintenance of stocks above the level which produces MSY in order to keep catch rates at an economic optimum.

To say nothing of a social optimum.

The Canadian position on yield and utilization is not laid out in draft fisheries articles as is that of the United States, though Canada did in 1972 introduce a working paper on living resources (UNGA 1972a) that contains these pertinent comments:

The objective of rational fishery management should be to constrain the productive capacity in a fishery, by controlling access, so that the yield is taken with no greater effort than necessary, taking into account, however, relevant social factors. This concept may be extended, and it could be envisaged that economic rationalization of fisheries would include the objective of obtaining maximum economic yield from resources.

Then at the end of the 1973 session, Canada submitted (anonymously, UNGA 1973e) a proposal relating to salmon that speaks of "the maintenance of such stocks at their optimum level."

Where does the rest of the world stand?

Of more than 20 fisheries proposals submitted during the LOS preparatory meetings only six, including that of the United States, dealt with yield concepts.

The draft articles submitted jointly by Australia and New Zealand and those submitted by Japan took positions close to the United States (UNGA 1972c; 1972d). The Australia-New Zealand articles placed responsibility on the coastal state ("within its zone of exclusive jurisdiction") to manage in such a way as to provide for the maximum sustainable yield. Japan said quite simply: "The objective of conservation measures is to achieve the maximum sustainable yields of fishery resources and thereby to secure and maintain a maximum supply of food and other marine products."

Afghanistan et al., in their proposal, spoke

of ". . . that part of the maximum allowable yield, as determined by the relevant international fisheries organization . . ." without defining the term "maximum allowable yield" (UNGA 1973c).

Ecuador, Panama, and Peru treated the subject indirectly in their proposal, requiring that regulations "shall ensure the conservation and rational utilization of living resources . . ." and "prevent indiscriminate exploitation" (UNGA 1973d).

Malta, in its articles dealing with "living resources of National Ocean Space," defined conservation of living resources as "the aggregate of measures rendering possible the optimum sustainable yield from such resources." It required conservation programs to be based on scientific findings and to include "measures of economic management" to give "maximum net returns in relation to potential sustained catch" (UNGA 1973b).

This is the sum total. However, the large group of nations supporting an exclusive economic (fisheries) zone probably felt no need to spell out conservation principles because these would be a matter for each sovereign to determine within its realm of exclusivity.

Certainly the weight of expressed international opinion came down strongly for MSY up to Caracas. Only Malta, with its generally idealistic approach to world ocean affairs, stood clearly for management for economic as well as biological goals.

And, not surprisingly, recreational fishing received no notice at all. Dr. M. B. Schaefer said it for sport fishing in 1966:

Nowhere in the Geneva Conventions, or elsewhere in the international law, so far as I can ascertain, is any special consideration given to the use of living resources of the sea for recreational purposes. Thus, any priority to the sports fisheries requires handling within the context of the maximum sustainable yield, unless some radical change of the practice of nations in this regard is possible, which I very much doubt.

What of Caracas? Several speakers have touched on last summer's Law of the Sea Conference, at which Ambassador Stevenson reiterated the basic U.S. position with respect to MSY and full utilization in a plenary speech. He said: "For fisheries, to the extent that the coastal state does not fully utilize a fishery resource, we contemplate a coastal state duty to permit foreign fishing under reasonable coastal state regulations." And, "the principle of full utilization will ensure that renewable resources which might not otherwise be utilized will give some benefit to the coastal state and help meet the international community's protein requirements."

Later in the session, the United States introduced new draft articles (United Nations 1974) that superceded our earlier fisheries position (UNGA 1972b). With respect to coastal stocks, they reiterated the principle of full utilization but qualified the concept of MSY to allow "taking into account . . . any generally agreed global and regional minimum standards" as well as "environmental and economic factors" and by adding this concept in the conservation article: "such measures shall take into account effects on species associated with or dependent upon harvested species and at a minimum, shall be designed to maintain or restore populations of such associated or dependent species above levels at which they may become threatened with extinction."

Nothing was decided at Caracas, and it remains to be seen what, if any, agreement can be reached in future sessions.

Postscript

A month after this symposium, Ambassador S. H. Amerasinghe, president of the Law of the Sea Conference, made a significant speech before FAO's Committee on Fisheries. He said (Food and Agricultural Organization 1974):

Although much stress is laid on the full utilization of fisheries resources so as to secure the maximum yield, Professor Colin Clark [an Australian economist] does not agree that the Maximum Sustainable Yield concept is economically sound in regard to fisheries exploitation. According to Professor Clark, there is no reason why the most efficient economic policy should automatically adopt the Maximum Sustainable Yield concept. On the other hand, the optimum yield concept would appear to be a much sounder one . . .
The rights and duties of the coastal State in the exclusive fisheries zone must be considered in regard to two aspects of the problem:
    1) conservation and management
    2) optimum utilization
In regard to migratory species or species which, in the course of their life span, move from one jurisdiction to another, . . . The States involved have a

duty to consult and co-operate with one another in determining the conservation measures and the optimum utilization standards, . . .

Commentary

Rather than try to reiterate and summarize the diverse, if not sometimes contradictory, points our speakers have made today, it seems more fruitful for me to make some general observations. These are based on and tempered by not only what has been said but on my thoughts in preparing for this symposium, during which time I was able to preview many of the drafts and to exchange ideas with participants and non-participants alike.

I am going mostly to use the term "optimum yield" which for today's purpose I define as

a deliberate melding of biological, economic, social, and political values designed to produce the maximum benefit to society from a given stock of fish.

This is not so different from what Roland Smith has called the optimum beneficial yield—"a yield in most cases below MSY, taking into account economic and social objectives." I said optimum yield rather than optimum sustainable yield quite deliberately, for as I visualize things, the optimum may *not* be a value we wish to sustain but in fact a variable that we deliberately choose to manipulate, down as well as up, and that for certain purposes we may wish to hold at levels that may *not* be sustainable indefinitely.

The optimum sustainable yield then becomes a subset of optimum yield representing

a deliberate melding of biological, economic, social and political values designed to produce the maximum benefit to society from stocks that are sought for human use, taking into account the effect of harvesting on dependent or associated species.

These definitions permit

(i) recognition of non-extractive uses and values,

(ii) allowance for the importance of quality to the sport fishing experience,

(iii) consideration of return on investment as a major criterion in setting harvest rates,

(iv) management on the basis of traditional

MSY if the need for fisheries products is overriding,

(v) tempering all these factors with knowledge of the real world and of what is acceptable to the body politic.

This gives us a flexible and pragmatic formula that can accommodate to the goals of any nation. It is a function of MSY, which remains a fundamental parameter needed for fisheries management in the sense that a knowledge of what we are doing to stocks, and where they are on the biological production curve, is essential in a rational decision-making process.

It is also a function of economics, and we need, equally badly, quantifications in economic terms. The introduction of social values brings intangibles into play that can only be evaluated subjectively at this point in time (but there are those who would say our estimates of physical and economic yield are often pretty subjective themselves). Optimum yield accommodates the concept Royce expressed in a 1972 paper of "a complete intergradation between the negative [e.g., nonconsumptive] and positive yield functions." It acknowledges the reality of political forces, no matter how much the purist may deplore their existence. It perhaps injures the dignity of some sacred cows, and may even impugn their integrity. But do we have to be efficient because economists say we should, or do we have to harvest for maximum physical production because it has become a dogma of fisheries science that it is somehow immoral to do otherwise?

How is this likely to work out in the real world?

1. The optimum yield will in certain fisheries be equal to the MSY. This will be particularly true for stocks under the control of nations to whom the need for protein is paramount.

Pragmatically, MSY is likely to govern, at least for the foreseeable future, in multinational fisheries prosecuted particularly by nations whose economic needs and social standards are widely variant. This raises a question about fisheries managed on a national quota basis. The International Commission for the Northwest Atlantic Fisheries (ICNAF) system of a two-tier quota, under which the allowable take from the total biomass is less than the sum of the allowable physical take from each of its component species, does not seem likely to lend itself to regulation on other than an MSY basis, in the sense that economic and social values cannot, now at least, be introduced into the equation. You can call it a form of optimum yield management based on MSY.

You can hypothesize an internationally managed fishery in which each member nation can manage its share of the agreed take in any way it wishes, including not catching everything allowed it for either economic or social reasons. It may seem a sheer dream to think that billfish might someday be managed in this manner for the benefit of both sport and commercial fishermen, but it is not necessarily that fantastic a thought. I point out that, for several years, conflict between U.S. sport fishermen and Japanese longliners in the eastern Pacific and the Gulf of Mexico has been minimal because of understandings reached between private parties in the two nations. If that could work, nothing is impossible. This leads me to another postulate.

2. *The optimum yield may approach zero harvest for substantial stocks that are demonstrated to fill essential niches in the food chain for more desirable species.* The northern anchovy off the California coast would fall in this category if the allegation that it fills such a niche is ever demonstrated and the socio-political judgment made that this is in fact the highest use of the resource. Mexico, however, might well choose to manage the the same stock off its Baja California coast for either maximum physical or maximum economic yield. This would put determination of an agreed optimum yield into the realm of international politics and negotiation. Under the present U.S. posture with respect to full utilization, Mexico (or anyone else desiring to fish for the difference between MSY and the existing catch) would win hands down. You can visualize a different settlement under different ground rules wherein the doctrine of full utilization did not apply. Assuming a

fifty-fifty split of the stock between the two countries, Mexico might limit its catch to half of the calculated MSY while the United States took nothing out of its half.

3. *The optimum yield will for many fisheries approximate the maximum net economic yield.* Nations will deliberately fish for dollars rather than for fish because economic need (or desire) is greater than the need for food. This is not necessarily confined to conventional commercial fishing. I can visualize certain of the lesser developed countries that happen to have the right combination of geography and big game fish choosing a recreational fishing industry catering to foreigners in preference to a commercial. I do not know whether our Mexican colleagues made a conscious choice a number of years ago with respect to the Gulf of California, but developments in Baja California Sur bear this theory out. Mexico has, I am sure, gained far more socially and economically by using the billfish, tuna, roosterfish, and their allies as bait for sportsmen than it could have by using them as a direct source of protein. The area has geography (proximity to foreign customers in the United States) scenery, climate, and game fish going for it. The situation is unusual, but not unique. And no doubt there are elsewhere undeveloped places and latent fisheries that would gain more by fishing for fishermen than for fish.

4. *The optimum yield may for limited periods exceed the MSY if economic or social demands so dictate*, this with the understanding that overdrafts from the biological bank have to be repaid or the fishery lost, at least in an economic sense. The extreme example of overfishing for social or economic reasons is the case wherein we might deliberately fish a stock down to a level of economic extinction as rapidly and efficiently as possible if maximum economic or social return would result from a short-term intensive fishery followed by a long-term period of stock recovery.

I have heard it suggested that the Pacific sardine fishery may unwittingly have followed this course during the 1930's. The argument goes like this: Society may have been served better by the intensive harvest rates because this was at the height of the Depression, every job was needed, and low-cost food was vital. The sardine fishery provided jobs and cheap protein; managed at MSY during this period the jobs would have been fewer and the supply of food less. Let me quickly add that it has been 20 years since the final collapse of the fishery, and the northern stock which was hit the hardest has not resurged and may in fact be dangerously near to biological extinction.

The soupfin shark is another example, but with a happier ending. It was overharvested at the time of World War II because it and the dogfish were the chief sources of vitamin A for the allied nations (the soupfin liver is the richest known natural source of this vitamin). The soupfin reached economic extinction at about the time synthetic vitamin A appeared. The population has come back, the species is again abundant—but virtually unfished. Careful husbanding of the resource (an academic proposition in time of war) would have meant cutting back the supply of a needed vitamin and, as it turned out, left a sizeable stock for which there would have been little use in the 1950's.

The sardine and soupfin were, of course, not managed with any thought of gaining optimum return through short-term intensive harvest. They were really not managed at all. But their case histories suggest that this sort of optimal management could be effective if done with forethought.

Looking ahead, the need for food in a lesser developed nation could be overriding, and understandably lead to deliberate overfishing as fishing strategies became available that were sufficiently sophisticated to permit high harvest rates from previously unharvested or underharvested subsistence fisheries.

5. *The optimum yield from certain fisheries will require harvest rates greater than the MSY of some of their component species, particularly in multispecies trawl fisheries.* This will result from conscious decisions that the greatest return to society will result from the incidental overharvesting of some species to permit the optimum sustainable harvest of others in either kilos or dollars.

The ICNAF stocks I mentioned a moment ago are candidates. The Pacific halibut fishery is another; one management option is to subject the species to incidental overharvesting in the Bering Sea to permit optimum harvest of other groundfish stocks.

6. *The optimum yield for some stocks will be that which will maintain only the minimum population necessary to ensure the species' continued existence.* Optimum yield may be greater than sustained physical yield of fish for which there is little or no human use at the time, and whose presence acts adversely on the abundance or the availability of target species. There could be intentional overfishing of "weed" species at an economic loss to permit greater abundance of, and harvest and return from, stocks with greater value as sources of food, income, or recreation.

This has often been suggested for marine species such as dogfish and skates, and lake and stream eradication programs for rough fish have been with us for a long time. This is perhaps best described as social management for optimum yield, with often a strong lacing of political factors. Very likely there is at least a long range economic payoff. What this approach says is that virtual extinction, at least locally, of certain species is proper management, and that optimum yield equals maximum physical, not maximum sustainable physical. No fisheries manager in this day and age would advocate a program leading to biological extinction of a stock, but holding it at a level below MSY for specific purposes is a legitimate application, always remembering that "maintenance of sufficient populations of all species of aquatic organisms to insure their continued existence" (California Fish and Game Code, Sec. 1700) is a basic responsibility.

7. *The optimum yield from the point of view of a country having control of a stock might be to let another nation harvest that stock at a predetermined rate in return for cash, credit, or some other sort of rights that might or might not be fishery-oriented.*

Under an international regime of exclusive coastal nation control, for example, the United States might do several things with respect to

Pacific pollock and other groundfish stocks in the eastern Bering Sea until it was ready to harvest them itself. It might, but probably wouldn't, allow foreign harvesting to continue unhampered. It might stop all foreign fishing forthwith. This is almost as unlikely. An option much more attractive to most observers is for the United States to sell its fishing rights to the highest bidder or exchange them for something we want more than pollock. Abstention from high seas harvest of salmon has been mentioned more than once.

8. *The optimum yield can be less than the conventional concept of maximum net economic yield for certain marine stocks of primary interest to sport fishermen in developed countries*, such as the United States and Canada. Management will be for social values, satisfaction in terms of catch rates and size of fish with due regard for the quality of the fishermen's environment. (But I wonder if the real economic return might not be as great or greater than it would be from the same stock managed as a maximum net economic yield commercial fishery.)

Most of our freshwater fisheries have long been managed for these social values, and the optimum yield has represented a balance between what the angler wanted in terms of satisfaction, what he was willing to pay in terms of a license, and what programs the responsible political entities chose to fund and implement.

9. *The optimum yield will be zero harvest for species considered to be of greatest value for their aesthetic interest (the California garibaldi), or for inhabitants of fragile environments that could be damaged by intrusion of man or his gear, or of environments that have high scenic values (coral reefs, underwater parks).*

10. *The optimum yield for "desirable" stocks that are already overharvested will range from zero up, depending on the level to which one desires to restore the stock and the speed with which one wants to reach that level.*

Optimum yield in these terms seems to offer what many of us have been looking for, and it boils down simply to giving people options,

options to consider values other than physical yield when circumstances so dictate. It is the inflexibility of MSY and the dogma of full utilization in the sense of maximum physical production that turns people off, not the validity of the concept, for as I have suggested, optimum yield will likely equal MSY in many fisheries for a long time to come.

In the real world of fisheries management we haven't really done so awfully well in maintaining stocks at a level of biological maximum yield when we have tried to. There are many reasons for this, but certainly important ones relate to the imposition of economic, social, and political forces into the system in an unplanned and frequently adversary manner. A change in rationale which will allow us to introduce these values into the yield equation in a deliberate and planned way should enable us to manage our fisheries resources far more effectively for the greatest public benefit.

Whether we have reached a consensus here today will have to stand the test of time, as those of us with managerial responsibilities go about our business. Certainly the speakers, the panelists, the audience, have all expressed their feelings, their ideas, their convictions, and this symposium has more than fulfilled its basic purpose of permitting an exposition of views and a debate of the issues. Robert Mauermann may have said it for everyone in his presentation: we have the same goal, though some of us may march to the sound of a different drummer.

A few months ago, when a small group of us first discussed the idea of this symposium, we expressed the hope that the proceedings of the meeting would form a landmark document in the evolution of fisheries yield concepts. There seems no question but that they will.

Scientific Names of Fish Mentioned in the Text

Anchovy, northern	*Engraulis mordax*
Dogfish, spiny	*Squalus acanthias*
Garibaldi	*Hypsypops rubicunda*
Halibut, Pacific	*Hippoglossus stenolepis*
Pollock, Pacific	*Theragra chalcogramma*
Roosterfish	*Nematistius pectoralis*
Sardine, Pacific	*Sardinops sagax*
Shark, soupfin	*Galeorhinus zyopterus*
Yellowtail	*Seriola dorsalis*

Literature Cited

BRYAN, R. C. 1974. The dimensions of a saltwater sport fishing trip or what do people look for in a fishing trip besides fish? Environment Canada, Fish. & Mar. Serv., So. Oper. Br, Pac. Reg., PAC/T-74-1. 35 pp.

CALIFORNIA DEPARTMENT OF FISH AND GAME. 1966. California fish and wildlife plan. State Printing Office, Sacramento. 3 vols.

CALIFORNIA UNIVERSITY. INSTITUTE OF MARINE RESOURCES. 1965. California and use of the ocean: a planning study of marine resources prepared for the California State Office of Planning. IMR Ref. 65-21. (various paging)

CHAPMAN, W. M. 1970. The theory and practices of international fishery development—management. San Diego Law Rev. 7(3): 408–454.

FOOD AND AGRICULTURE ORGANIZATION OF THE UNITED NATIONS. 1974. Address by H. E. Ambassador Shirley Hamilton Amerasinghe. Committee on Fisheries, doc COFI/74/Inf. 9. 8 pp.

HERRINGTON, W. C., T. CLINGAN, AND L. WAKEFIELD. 1973. Marine life. N.Y. Acad. Sci., Ann. 216: 95–104.

INTERNATIONAL ASSOCIATION OF GAME, FISH AND CONSERVATION COMMISSIONERS. 1973. Resolution 7. Pages 257–258 in Report of the Resolutions Comm. Int. Assoc. Game, Fish and Cons. Comm., 63rd Convention.

LARKINS, H. A. 1973. The U.S. proposal for the Law of the Sea Conference. The U.S. fishery position and the law of the sea. Statement presented to Am. Fish. Soc., 103 Ann. Meet., Orlando, Fla., 13 Sept. 73.

POLLOCK, H. W. 1973. Statement by the Honorable Howard W. Pollock, U. S. Representative in Subcommittee II, of the Committee on the Peaceful Uses of the Seabed and the Ocean Floor. U.S. Mission to the United Nations, New York, April 3, 1973. 13 pp.

ROEDEL, P. M. 1969. A consideration of the living marine resources off California and the factors affecting their use. Calif. Mar. Res. Comm., Calif. Coop. Ocean. Fish. Invest., Rept., 13: 19–23.

ROYCE, W. F. 1972. The gap between theory and policy in fishery development. Pages 156–163 in World fisheries policy, multidisciplinary views. Univ. Wash. Press, Seattle and London.

SCHAEFER, M. B., chairman. 1966. Symposium on the appropriate role of limitation of entry as a method of managing marine fisheries, app. IV. Pages 50–115 in Proceedings of the Fifth Meeting, Governor's Advisory Commission on Ocean Resources. Calif. Dept. Finance, State Off. of Planning, Sacramento.

SPORT FISHING INSTITUTE. 1974. SFI Directors' resolutions. SFI Bull. 255: 1–3.

STEVENSON, J. R. 1972. Statement by the Honorable John R. Stevenson. U. S. Info. Serv., U. S. Mission, Geneva, August 10, 1972. 5 pp.

———. 1974. An address before the plenary session of the Law of the Sea Conference Mar. Fish. Rev. 36(8): 1–4.

UNITED NATIONS. 1974. United States of America: draft articles for a chapter on the economic zone and the continental shelf. 3rd Conf. Law of the Sea. Doc. A/Conf.62/C.2/L.47. 11 pp.

UNITED NATIONS GENERAL ASSEMBLY. 1971. Draft articles on the breadth of the territorial sea, straits, and fisheries submitted by the United States. Doc. A/AC.138/SC.II/L.4. 30 July, 1971. Pages 241–245 in Report of the Committee on the peaceful uses of the sea-bed and the ocean floor beyond the limits of national jurisdiction. 26th sess., Sup. 21 (A/8421).

———. 1972a. Management of the living resources of the sea. Working paper submitted by Canada. Doc. A/AC.138/SC.II/L.8. 27 July 1972. 11 pp. Also in Report of the Committee on the peaceful uses of the sea-bed and the ocean floor beyond the limits of national jurisdiction. 27th Sess., Sup. 21 (A/8721).

———. 1972b. United States revised draft fisheries article. Doc. A/AC.138/SC.II/L.9. 4 August 1972. 5 pp. Ibid.

———. 1972c. Working paper by the delegations of Australia and New Zealand. Principles for a fisheries regime. Doc. A/AC.138/SC.II/L.11. 11 August 1972. 5 pp. Ibid.

———. 1972d. Proposals for a regime of fisheries on the high seas, submitted by Japan. Doc. A/AC.138/SC.II/L.12. 14 August 1972. 10 pp. Ibid.

———. 1973a. Special considerations regarding the management of anadromous fishes and highly migratory oceanic fishes: working paper submitted by the United States of America. Doc. A/AC.138/SC.II/L.20. 2 April 1973. Pages 11–19 in Report of the Committee on the peaceful uses of the seabed and the ocean floor beyond the limits of national jurisdiction. 28th sess., Sup. 21 (A/9021) Vol. III.

———. 1973b. Malta: Preliminary draft articles. . . . Doc. A/AC.138/SC.II/L.28. 16 July 1973. Ibid. pages 35–70.

———. 1973c. Afghanistan, Austria, Belgium, Bolivia, Nepal and Singapore: Draft articles on resource jurisdiction of coastal states beyond the territorial sea. Doc. A/AC.138/SC.II/L.39. 16 July 1973. Ibid. pages 85–86.

———. 1973d. Ecuador, Panama, and Peru: Draft articles on fisheries in national and international zones in ocean space. Doc. A/AC.138/SC.II/L.54. 10 August 1973. Ibid. pages 107–109.

———. 1973e. Working group of the whole. Conf. Room paper No. 22, 7.3 Fisheries. Page 134 in Rept. of the Committee on the peaceful uses of the seabed and the ocean floor beyond the limits of national jurisdiction. 29th Sess., Sup. 21 (A/9021) Vol. IV.

Office of Marine Resources, National Oceanic and Atmospheric Administration, United States Department of Commerce, Rockville, Maryland 20852